The
TWILIGHT
Phenomenon

Nicola Bardola studied German at university, then worked as an editor and wrote for various newspapers. Since 1985 he has been working in children's and youth literature and is passionate about encouraging children to read. He was editor-in-chief for a specialist journal for youth media and for several years he has published an annual list recommending the fifty best books for children and young adults.

THE UNOFFICIAL
COMPANION TO THE
BESTSELLING VAMPIRE SERIES

The TWILIGHT Phenomenon

Nicola Bardola

Translated by Solveig Emerson

PICCADILLY PRESS • LONDON

First published in Great Britain in 2009
by Piccadilly Press Ltd,
5 Castle Road, London NW1 8PR
www.piccadillypress.co.uk

Text copyright © Nicola Bardola, 2009
English language translation © Solveig Emerson
Translated from the original *Bestseller Mit Biss.
Liebe, Freundschaft und Vampire –
alles über die Autorin Stephenie Meyer*
published by Wilhelm Heyne Verlag, München
a division of Verlagsgruppe Random House GmbH,
München, Germany

A catalogue record for this book is available
from the British Library

ISBN: 978 1 84812 071 6

3 5 7 9 10 8 6 4 2

Printed in the UK by Bookmarque CPI, Croydon, CR0 4TD
Cover design by Simon Davis
Cover photo © Getty Images

Contents

The moment her regard ceased,
I would have torn his heart out,
and drank his blood!

Emily Brontë, *Wuthering Heights*

FOREWORD

Stephenie Meyer, answering a question about possible sequels to her four *Twilight* bestsellers, speaks of a Cullen universe having come to life. Since this is an intricate saga, there are numerous possibilities in Bella and Edward Cullen's lives that might become her new starting point. The 2,379 pages of the four *Twilight* books deal with big emotional themes from a teenage perspective: love, hate, death and immortality being only a few of the central topics which are woven into a thrilling story. The supernatural is never made more important than reality. Stephenie Meyer builds fantasy into the love story between Bella and Edward in such a way that the reader can always find links with daily life and to real situations.

This book is designed to be a companion volume to Stephenie Meyer's *Twilight* saga. If you have already read the four *Twilight* books, this book will remind you of the incomparable passion of the protagonists and reawaken your own feelings experienced on reading the stories for the first time. If, on the other hand, you are a new reader wondering whether to give in to the draw of the *Twilight* saga, this book will provide you with many reasons to do just that. A word of warning though: I shall be discussing the whole of Bella and Edward's love story. If you want to keep the suspense of the unknown, read the whole saga first!

I hope this book sheds some new light on the *Twilight* saga and on the extraordinary fascination it exerts.

Nicola Bardola

Inspiration

In the Beginning
There Was a Dream

June 2nd, 2003 is now the stuff of legend: Stephenie Meyer, housewife and mother of three young sons, wakes up one morning with the memory of a dream still in her mind; a dream she cannot and will not forget. This dream is to change both her life and the lives of millions of readers across the world. Stephenie sits down and puts her dream into writing. Almost unchanged, this becomes the chapter *Confessions* in the first book of the *Twilight* series: a beautiful, cold vampire glitters in the sunlight. A girl falls head over heels in love, forever. The legend of Bella and Edward is born. The lead-up to this moment, the meeting of the two main characters as students at Forks High School, their slow coming together, all this is still to follow.

Five years later, on a Monday morning at 9.23 a.m. on a train going to Cologne Literary Festival, I get an interview with Stephenie Meyer. As we turn into a bend the train crunches over the tracks. Given how well documented Stephenie Meyer's love of sports cars is, we really ought to be sitting in a softly purring Porsche. The dedication to her fans in *Eclipse* reads, *I wish I could give you each a big hug and a Porsche 911 Turbo.*

I'm sitting opposite her in a train carriage and have two hours for the interview. I sit back, enjoying the atmosphere and ask whether her next reading tour of Germany might not be speedier in a sports car. 'I'd love to visit the Porsche factory. In Italy, I got to drive a Ferrari a few times. And I drive fast!' laughs the bestselling author from the driving town of Phoenix, where 'the nearest supermarket is twenty miles from home'. At home in the US she currently drives a spacious estate car, ideal for a family of five. She hasn't got her Infiniti G35 Coupé any more, but it won't be too long before she gets herself another sporty number. 'When I was a teenager, while all my friends were staring at boys, I was staring at fast cars.' Stephenie comes across as natural and spontaneous. She has a bright laugh and pauses now and again to gather her thoughts. She wears no make-up despite having known in advance about the interview and photo-shoot taking place on the train. The clip on the recording cable is missing, so she improvises quickly, fixing the mike to her red dress using a hairclip. She almost always wears red, even in press photos, but she doesn't, she insists, have a favourite colour (nor a favourite word). She finds it embarrassing that there's a picture on the internet showing her in an atmospheric, gothic setting, wearing red, of course. But it's true that Stephenie's appearance – her arched eyebrows, her full mouth, her shining red hair, the laughter lines – has something a little fantastic about it, which makes her theme of vampires and werewolves seem not entirely coincidental.

That dream was the beginning of everything: the couple in a clearing. An everyday girl and a beautiful vampire. At the time she had that all-important dream, circumstances weren't all that easy: her husband was ill, she had a broken arm and her thirtieth birthday was looming. 'It was certainly an odd time, though not what I'd call a crisis,' she says. Can she really not remember any kind of trigger for this dream? She appears decisive: 'I had never seen a vampire film. I don't know where the dream came from. Maybe a TV advert put me in mind of it, or a fragment of conversation, I just don't know – I can't remember any particular reason.'

Whatever prompted it, the following morning she wrote down her dream and then continued to write a little every day – usually at night – until by the end of August 2003 the manuscript was complete.

By November 2003, she had already received a lucrative contract for the film script. Soon afterwards *Twilight* knocked J.K. Rowling's *Harry Potter* off the top spot in the *New York Times* Bestseller list and began to be translated into many languages across the world.

'The fans everywhere respond the same way: they're

enthusiastic and ask all the same questions – everyone's interested in the same things. My books deal with life not death, love not violence, which is also the reason for my success,' says Stephenie, who doesn't feel at all obliged to stick to a horror genre. She had hardly any prior knowledge of vampire mythology, as a result of which her characterisation of Edward Cullen and his family has successfully created a fascinating and effective new breed of vampire.

'For me the characters are really real! They have developed a life of their own. I even talk to them when I'm alone in the car,' Stephenie assures me quite believably. The intensity with which she shares in this *amour fou* – this unique love-triangle between Bella, Edward and Jacob, between human, vampire and werewolf – is palpable in her writing. 'I write about characters who are real to me, even though they are of course fictitious heroes in a novel. But they do think about the kinds of things which interest me in real life.'

Could the vampire characters she portrays be seen as better, even perfect people? 'I wouldn't describe Edward as perfect. Perhaps his "father", Carlisle, who really tries hard to be a good person. But even he has moments of self-doubt. The only difference between good and bad people, in my opinion, is that good people keep trying to be good, whereas bad people just give up and say "What's the point?" Good people aren't perfect though, they can't ever be perfect.' So perhaps they *are* a little like Stephenie Meyer's vampires? 'No, I don't see my vampires as projections of an ideal person to be looked up to,' she states.

Stephenie was born at Christmas, which has given her a rather negative opinion of birthdays. Only once, for her tenth birthday, did her mother organise a party. 'It's hard to celebrate a birthday and Christmas at the same time. That's why I don't like my birthday. Although now it's more of an advantage – hardly anyone notices I've grown another year older. I don't have to organise any birthday parties for myself. It's almost as though I never grow any older,' she says and grins. 'I really don't like getting older. But you just have to come to terms with it,' says Stephenie. A lot like Bella, then, who wants to appear the same age as Edward forever, and Stephenie does confess to sharing a number of Bella's personality traits, like fainting at the sight of blood (but no, she wasn't at the doctor's surgery on June 1st, 2003). 'There are so many lovely things associated with mortality: a growing family, grandparents. Vampires can't have children – at least not the female ones.' Stephenie smiles mischievously (the fourth book was still a strict secret when this conversation took place). 'Life has to do with change, with cycles. Every human being changes. Vampires, on the other hand, never age, don't change – some may find that desirable, others don't like the thought. Personally, I think every phase of life should be enjoyed. There are many women who dress like teenagers, or have plastic surgery and do a whole range of other things to themselves to stay looking young. I'm in my thirties now, my children are great: I'm enjoying it.'

Stephenie is a Mormon and as such believes that there is life after death. 'Yes, my books could be seen as offering new interpretations of aspects of religion, but that wasn't my intention.' A central theme in the *Twilight* series is not having sex before marriage. 'I can tell from the reaction of my readers how great the longing for romantic relationships is. Children today are often made to grow up very fast. There's not much time for innocence. Innocence has been lost. I think people often miss out on the pleasure to be found in desiring something. But the readers' reaction to the relationship between Bella and Edward tells me what great longing there is for this type of innocent relationship. I hope that my stories re-establish something of this romance. Why shouldn't people enjoy the holding-hands stage and go back to letting that bit last a little longer? There are so many wonderful stages in romantic relationships, which get missed out nowadays.' But how can Bella and Edward ever develop their relationship? Must Edward become human? She laughs captivatingly: 'I can't tell you that! I can't give the ending away!' But she does give away that the fourth book will be the longest, at around 750 pages. 'In October 2003, I already knew how it would all end, as the finale is one of the many epilogues I [wrote but] didn't use at the end of book one, some of which did become books two and three. I hope people will be understanding when they read the last book and let me finish the story the way I want to.'

The ending is now public and has led to fierce controversy. More about that later, but first, I want to know from the author how she feels about three central aspects of her *Twilight* saga.

Stephenie addresses the theme of love. 'Was there ever a more romantic love than Bella's? She's not a vampire and for a number of reasons can't be together with Edward. That's the Romeo-and-Juliet effect: something obstructs the path of true love, meaning the lovers must then ask themselves what each is willing to sacrifice for the sake of being with the person they love. For Bella, it is her life. Every time she is with Edward, her life is in danger. Could love be any more passionate?'

Next, I want to know how Stephenie sees good and evil. 'I grew up in a community where being a good and well-behaved girl was not the exception. It was expected. All of my friends, both female and male were also good and well-behaved. That had to do with my religion, with being a Mormon. That's why there aren't really any villains in my stories. And if there are, they have good reason to be villainous. I don't think the world is so full of bad people.' It's a view that reveals that Stephenie's faith sees power and revenge as the most frequent causes of violence.

And lastly the major question: why vampires? 'Vampires fascinate me because of their dual nature. People like to be frightened. That's why horror books and films are so successful: zombies and witches and so on are generally scary figures. We are afraid of them. We are afraid of vampires too, because they want to kill us. But, on the other hand, we also admire them because they have many advantages. They have eternal youth, are usually beautiful and attractive, intelligent, sensitive, live in castles and so on. We want what they have, but we're afraid of what they want.'

After this we talk about writing. 'I never deliberately work important themes into my stories. I don't see my books as receptacles for opinions or beliefs that I could share with my readers. No, I write my books purely to entertain the readers, and I'm happy if the readers enjoy them. But equally I'm not upset if, having read my books, they have a new and nicer idea of love.'

And, almost by chance, Stephenie created a whole new breed of vampire. I want to know whether looking back on it she would change anything. 'No, I would do exactly the same again. It's more fun to invent something of your own – I don't know anything about the whole vampire mythology. It's all fun!'

Stephenie emphasises how passionate she is about reading – rarely non-fiction, she prefers the novels referred to in her *Twilight* saga. She talks about her literature degree, emphasising that she didn't really study creative writing. 'For my degree I had to take one class in creative writing and I chose poetry. I did attend, but I only pretended to participate.' She tells me that she always wrote stories, but never thought they were any good. At eighteen, she did finally write a few poems. 'My parents thought it would be a good thing for me if I kept a diary. So I did, but without enthusiasm and only to get the reward – my driver's licence. I was furious that they were forcing me to do it, but I played along. As you'd expect, the stuff I wrote in it was pretty negative. Well, I suppose teenagers are prone to such outbursts.'

My conversation with the creator of Bella and Edward forms the basis of my reflections on her *Twilight* saga. Stephenie revealed a great deal in our conversation, things which aren't on either her own or other websites. And yet I didn't succeed in entering into her thinking as deeply as I'd hoped to. Every time I tried to address the many serious themes in her books, she would avoid my question. Suddenly it seemed to me that Stephenie had one particular similarity to Bella: no one can read her thoughts. Stephenie, like the transformed Bella in *Breaking Dawn*, can produce a shield which no one is going to break. But Stephenie Meyer's defence mechanisms have an up-side. She directs the reader away from herself, from her life and back towards the books. Only in the stories themselves are conclusions to be sought and found.

BELLA AND EDWARD

THE SECRET OF ETERNAL LOVE

Stefanie Perstat works in a bookshop and lives with her boyfriend Patrick and approximately 3,000 books. When she's not reading or travelling, she writes articles and reviews for specialist journals and collects knick-knacks from her other passions – surfing and Hawaii. In spring 2006 she wrote to me describing her reaction to the first volume of the *Twilight* saga. It was an early, impressive testament to Meyer-obsession.

'Oh no, yet another vampire novel – Anne Rice for teenagers! This sigh was probably to be heard going up from every reader as Stephenie Meyer's *Twilight* was delivered to the shops. But the effective cover design and the mysterious blurb already hinted that there was more excitement between the covers than we could have dared hope for. And so, after much insistence on the part of my colleague, I borrowed a copy from the publisher, only to return it two days later, completely read and

with a request for a copy of my very own.

'I neither could nor would be without Edward ever again, Bella had become my best friend and I could feel the drizzling rain of Forks trickling over my skin. The English-language audio book and paperback followed seamlessly on from this and, if I had been living in Arizona, I would have gone to "I love Edward" parties and worn T-shirts with the same message.

'What begins as a teenage rites of passage novel (the protagonist, Bella, moves from Phoenix, Arizona to live with her father in the small and rainy town of Forks) seamlessly and quickly turns into a love story that tingles on the skin like Edward's dangerous kisses.

'Bella, who could actually have the pick of any boy in her class and has to keep dealing with the advances of her classmates, soon tastes the forbidden fruit: Edward Cullen, a boy often strangely distant, of heavenly beauty and with changing eye-colour, who, along with his "siblings" fills first her dreams, then her life. After a brief hesitation, a passion develops between them, which could be fatal for Bella: Edward is a vampire and it is only his intense love for the mortal Bella that keeps him from turning her into his immortal companion. But does Bella want him to continue his existence alone? Haven't things already gone too far for that?

'This is the love story told in Stephenie Meyer's debut novel. This book is a true page-turner, because while familiar and well-established elements of high school are to be found framing the story, this form of vampire tale is the first of its kind without extravagantly described love scenes or bloodthirstiness. Every page breathes pain and longing, but without cliché. You'll laugh, cry and thirst for each new page and each meeting, as Edward thirsts for Bella's blood and Bella for an eternal life with him. You'll suffer with them, knowing the danger yet powerless to fight it. The language, however, remains so simple and poetic, realistic and contemporary that events lose their threatening danger and it becomes a sweet temptation to think that there might indeed be vampires living among us.'

It's an apt description of how many readers felt at the beginning of the saga. But what makes readers thirst after each further meeting of Edward and Bella and recommend this previously unknown author so enthusiastically that her books fast became international bestsellers?

ATTRACTION

When my unbiased companion, who had never read a single line of a *Twilight* book came out of the cinema having watched the film, she said in bewilderment, 'Why does she *want* him?' She emphasised the verb and meant Kristen Stewart, the actress with a slightly nervous blink who plays Bella, and the gorgeous Robert Pattinson, who plays Edward. 'Why does *she* want *him* of all people?' That is one of the central questions of the *Twilight* saga, in the film as well as the books. Which develops first out of love, passion and friendship? Why do these emotions happen with some people and not others? And how different are these emotions really?

To better understand Bella's feelings, it helps to look at the language she uses to describe Edward and the qualities that make him so attractive to her. There are many characteristics that make Edward the most perfect person on the planet according to Bella:

Edward's movements are strikingly elegant, his gait graceful.

His face is stunning and of a heavenly beauty, like in the glossy pages of a magazine or an Old Masters painting or like a character out of a film; a face every male model on the planet would give his soul for. It's the face of an angel, quite simply too beautiful to be true. The greatest compliment she can pay his face is that it stops her from looking at his body. In rare moments, his features can change dramatically and suddenly form 'a mask of deep, ancient grief'. His face can also be 'hard and statue-like'.

Edward's hair is the colour of bronze and often tousled, but when it's wet and windswept – in Forks a nearly daily (and nightly) occurrence – it still looks like it's just been styled for a hair-product advert.

Edward's forehead curves softly, and his cheekbones are pronounced. His nose is perfectly formed – straight and narrow – and he has a prominent chin.

His eyelashes are black, thick and long; sometimes they throw long shadows across his cheeks, and there are often shadows under his eyes, sometimes purplish, like a bruise.

His eyes can be similarly dark – varying from matt black to

an unusual ochre, 'darker than butterscotch but with the same golden tone'. They are jewel-like, they can glow and have a hypnotic quality and unleash a spectacular power – Bella experiences Edward's gaze as something elemental, sometimes pushing her to breaking point. She often simply doesn't know how to interpret the way he looks at her.

Edward's lips are gently arched and full. They are as hard as marble, yet somehow gentle. They are as smooth as if they had been polished, and part to reveal two perfect, gleaming white rows of teeth. His smile is shockingly seductive, his tongue as cold as ice as it follows the line of Bella's lips after kissing her.

Edward's fingers are long and pale and his lower arms are unexpectedly hard and muscular, just like his chest.

His skin is described as iridescent, smooth as silk and cold as stone. The pale patterns of his blue veins are visible on the insides of his lower arms. Edward can only go out into the sunshine when he's alone or if the observer is privy to his secret. When he first shows Bella what he looks like in the sun, it's a surprise: his skin is white as chalk and it sparkles, as though it were studded all over with countless tiny diamonds. He is a statue of perfection, carved from an unknown stone: as smooth as marble, glittering like crystal.

Edward's clothes are not often described by Bella. At their first dinner together in Port Angeles, Edward is wearing a pale-brown leather jacket and a tight, ivory-coloured turtle-neck jumper, which emphasises his muscular chest.

Overall, Bella describes his appearance as immaculate;

Edward is as beautiful as a dream with an almost magnetic attraction. She can't find anything about him which could be improved: he is too perfect.

Bella frequently describes him as a god-like creature, and he has many attributes that suggest this too.

Edward's voice can be irresistibly soft and silken. Sometimes it is like honey, sometimes like 'a single, crackling call' at the sound of which Bella can forget to breathe, her heart beating wildly, and she's in danger of hyperventilating or passing out. When Edward hums the lullaby he composed for Bella, his voice seems to her to be 'the voice of an archangel'. His choice of words is particularly elegant and is more suited to a *fin-de-siècle* novel than a twenty-first century classroom. Sometimes he sounds more like a 'knight from a past century'.

Edward's breath makes Bella feel just as faint, since it has the most exquisite scent which clings to his clothes as well, only in a less intense form. When she feels his breath in her face, it dazes her pleasantly and clouds her mind. It is a sweet scent, not like any other Bella knows.

Edward's sense of smell, on the other hand, is so highly developed that each person smells quite individual to him. Bella smells unique and releases in him the strongest desire to act on his vampire instinct. It takes a few agonising weeks for him to get himself under control. But there are still many relapses. The first time he is with Bella in her bedroom, their intimacy leads him into temptation. He attempts to explain his problem to Bella by using alcohol as a metaphor. Giving up wine, he says, doesn't mean not being able to appreciate the bouquet. Bella, he says, has a floral scent, of lavender or freesias.

You would think Edward would worry about being so different to Bella, but he finds it easy to be himself around her, despite looking like a model at all times! The differences he shows in his vampiric nature and skills especially run the risk of alienating him from Bella, and the reader, but are presented in such a way that they too increase the attraction of his character.

When Edward asks Bella about her age, his voice sounds upset and, though she doesn't yet understand why, the reader already suspects the reason behind his sadness. On the journey back to Forks from Port Angeles the topic of Edward's age is brought up for the first time. He tells her he is seventeen. Quick as a flash and primed by her internet research, Bella asks how long he has been seventeen. 'A while,' Edward admits. A little while later, Bella hears that Carlisle has recently celebrated his three-hundred-and-sixty-second birthday.

The topic of age and death is a constant presence in current debates about our ageing society. In a light-hearted way, the *Twilight* saga helps the reader think seriously about the twilight of life. Again and again, Bella tries to impress upon Edward that she is ageing, that her death is coming closer with every passing minute (made most apparent by her eighteenth birthday at the beginning of *New Moon*) and that this will divide them. They have the option to change that. Edward must transform her, but he calls his existence an 'eternal night' and wants to spare Bella this. This chasm between them could have split them apart, but instead eventually serves to bind them together for an eternity where time stands still for them both.

Before she knows the truth, Bella suggests Edward might be a superhero, and he does have many super-powers that make him all the more appealing. Edward can track the scent of a human being or animal, can see at great distances and can't easily be wounded. He can read thoughts and find people within a radius of a few miles, once he has heard or seen their thoughts, and the more familiar a voice is to Edward, the greater the distance at which he can still hear it. It is a form of telepathy that Edward can use with everybody – except Bella. She is immune to Edward's mind-reading, a source of frustration to Edward and entertainment to the reader, such as when he checks up on Bella indirectly by reading the minds of the people she's talking to. Edward doesn't know why he can't hear Bella's thoughts. He thinks maybe her brain works differently to other people's, as though she were transmitting on an AM frequency when he can only receive FM. Edward's telepathy, and its limitation with Bella, makes him attractive to her in a number of ways. For example, he can read Charlie's thoughts, so Bella always knows in advance how she needs to behave towards her father. She, on the other hand, can keep secrets from Edward, which sometimes annoys him, but in dangerous situations proves to be a help. It's also interesting to note that this also makes Bella very unique to Edward.

Another super-power is Edward's strength, especially when it is combined with his incredible speed. The first significant demonstration of this comes in the *Confessions* chapter. Edward circles the meadow in a split second, effortlessly breaks a branch nearly a metre wide from a tree, balances it in the palm of his hand and hurls it at another tree. Edward demonstrates that he is the perfect predator, letting Bella see behind his façade. She, however, finds these qualities, and his outburst of violence, more seductive than frightening and finds him even more enticing.

In true superhero style, Edward first saves Bella's life (then again and again) in the icy car park of Forks High School. In a lightning quick move, too fast for the human eye and very reminiscent of scenes from *Superman*, Edward protects Bella from the out-of-control truck, saving her from certain death.

When Edward speeds through the forest, leaping from tree to tree with Bella on his back, it again echoes scenes of a heroine flying with Superman, although Bella feels like she's clinging to a stone and for the first time is frightened in his presence. Because Edward moves at such speed, it is like he is flying through the dark and thick undergrowth of the forest, 'like a bullet, like a ghost'. The whole journey is soundless and Edward shows no signs whatsoever of having made the least effort in it.

So, if Edward is at once an accomplished Romeo and Superman, how can Bella be Juliet and keep up with him? Why does he want *her*? What's *her* attraction? Although Bella sees herself as average – including her physical charms – the people around her see her as considerably more than average – most boys she meets in Forks are keen to ask her out. But Bella thinks of herself as so entirely ordinary that she can't believe she could be meant for someone like Edward. His strength and his beauty cause her many a pang at the difference between them, and make her feel sad. It is not until the last third of *Twilight* that Bella reveals that, in a relationship, she expects the man and the woman to be equals. She feels it shouldn't always be one person rescuing the other – they have to be able to rescue each other equally. This is the reason for her persistence in wanting to become a vampire, which determines the course of the saga. Whenever Edward notices this there is tension between them.

But it shows one of the many personality traits that Edward adores about Bella – and is more attractive to him than anything else. The fact that he cannot read her thoughts, that her responses to a situation are often very different to what Edward expects and that she has an irresistible scent adds to the attraction; but he doesn't know how to convince her of what he sees in her as a human being – everything he has ever held dear and wanted in a person. She is his soulmate, and simply cannot be more perfect to him.

PERSISTENCE

The attraction is a well-spun story in itself. When Edward first looks at Bella, the result is spine-tingling. The first, tentative contact between them consists of brief exchanges of glances. When Edward's gaze first flickers over to Bella, he quickly looks away again, much more quickly than Bella is able to, even though she drops her eyes immediately in embarrassment.

The first exchange of glances, then, consists of their both looking away from one another at lightning speed. Bella comments on this first wordless encounter as it's puzzling to her. At first Edward's glance appears uninterested, but the second exchange is different. This time his look seems to hold a sort of unfulfilled expectation, a slight frustration. The third time his look is hostile. The fourth time it's piercing, full of hatred. No wonder Bella's confused! Bella and Edward don't yet know each other, but their eye contact passes through dramatic phases, and the reader is also on hot coals to know how their silent contact will develop. On the one hand, particularly in Bella's case, the eye contact follows the familiar pattern of first love: realising you are looking at a soulmate, then looking away in shyness, or even fear, only then to look again to check you were not mistaken the first time. But Edward's behaviour does not fit this pattern. The reader can guess why, but this only adds to the pleasure of seeing how he chooses to react.

Edward's look can be burning and filled with overpowering strength or often just indescribable. During their arguments after Tyler's truck nearly crushed her, Edward and Bella glare at one another furiously. She finds it difficult to resist Edward's angry and glorious face: 'It was like trying to stare down a destroying angel,' thinks Bella to herself. She has the feeling she's almost always in the weaker position in these staring matches, as though hypnotised, unable to avert her gaze. This leads to phrases such as, 'when his eyes released me'.

So, Edward can hold Bella prisoner with his eyes. Especially when he's looking at her searchingly, curious and a little frustrated because he can't read her thoughts.

The description of the flirting between Bella and Edward is realistic and infectious, detailed and sensitive. This is where the quality of the story is to be seen, more complex and considerably more convincing than other high school love stories.

One example is the fact that Bella has three high school admirers: Eric, Mike and Tyler. She describes them as unwanted, though; Edward is the only one she's ever interested in, but he is very inconsistent in his early behaviour towards her.

When they're arguing, Edward's flawless appearance silences her again and again. Sometimes she wants to look at him angrily, but she finds it difficult to remain cross. Yet she is the one who initiates the first flirting: in the restaurant in Port Angeles it's Bella who touches the back of his hand with her fingertips, only to discover with a shock that his skin is cold and as hard as stone; although in the biology class, it was Edward who first touched her hand which Bella felt like an electric shock.

Their first kiss is not particularly romantic though: Edward seems to just want to try it out. Bella notices the way he takes her face in his hands and hesitates, but not in a human way – not waiting for silent permission, nor to prolong the anticipation that is '. . . sometimes better than the kiss itself' according to Bella. Edward's hesitation is to test himself, to check whether he has his craving under control.

When Edward's cold, marble lips finally meet hers, there is a surprising reaction – Bella gasps, grasps his hair, pulls him towards her and parts her lips to breathe in his scent. Her actions affect him so much that he has to push her back a few inches and take a moment to recover.

He is still wavering, unsure of whether his vampire desires might overpower his emotional ones, whether he might lose control or whether he's strong enough to resist his thirst for her blood. Later he knows it's merely a question of willpower.

It is details like these that really compel the reader to see the level on which Bella and Edward connect, and to enjoy the evolution of their relationship.

OLD-FASHIONED PASSION

Stephenie Meyer's way of describing the gloriousness of love is quite wonderful. Various difficulties, insecurities and annoyances are part of first love. Edward admits he's jealous of Mike. Bella awakens his human feelings. Although he's lived almost one hundred years amongst his own kind and humans, he says he never felt incomplete, but he didn't know there was something he was inadvertently searching for.

If Edward weren't a vampire, he could be described as

searching for himself. Edward remembers his human youth. He already felt himself to be a man then, not, however, searching for a woman, but preparing to become a soldier. After Carlisle made him a vampire, he didn't become a soldier, but worryingly for his 'parents' stayed single for many decades – despite many matchmaking attempts and a host of admirers. Until, that is, he sees and smells Bella. It is notable that it's not only Bella but also Edward who's in love for the first time. And so, like her, he often feels uncertain as their relationship grows closer.

Esme and Carlisle are overjoyed that he has finally fallen in love. They are happy that he is happy. The decades of abstinence made them worry that he had been changed too young, that 'something was missing' for him. What his foster-parents mean by this is not explained, but it hints that the *Twilight* saga may move on from innocent teenage romance.

Once Edward has confessed that, from the start, he'd secretly spent almost every night in her bedroom, they spend their first proper night together. Her pyjamas consist of a holey T-shirt and a pair of grey jogging trousers. They sit on her bed, exchanging caresses and Bella brings up the subject of weddings and marriage. Basically it's the same as for humans, Edward says. The Cullens share human desires, although these are often obscured by more powerful vampiric desires. Without actually saying the word, Bella asks about sex. Edward rejects the idea, because Bella's so fragile and breakable. One uncontrolled movement and he could cause her serious injury, so he can never lose control in her presence. So sex, as things stand, seems out of the question.

Both confess that they have never had sex. Edward, being a mind-reader, knows that love and lust don't always go hand in hand. It's not until the fourth volume, more suited to the fifteen and over age group, that this tension is resolved.

The first romantic relationships that develop at Forks High School are very innocent. Seventeen year olds who drive to school in their own car, park in their own parking spaces, but are far shyer in their flirting than most fourteen year olds in teen fiction – or in reality. That's clearly to do with Bella and Edward's character types – one shy and naïve, the other old-fashioned, in the literal sense – and of course also with Stephenie's own way of thinking.

Bella is surprised that Eric and Mike fancy her and that because of her there is even rivalry between them. In Phoenix the boys never looked at her twice. She thinks it may have to do with the Phoenix boys probably only ever seeing her as the young girl she had been. She also decides that the Forks boys see her clumsiness, for some unfathomable reason, as cute rather than pathetic. Later Tyler becomes her third unwanted admirer. All three invite her to the Spring Ball. She could have turned them down, which might have upset the boys, but Bella decides to do a bit of matchmaking. When Bella notices that Jessica secretly fancies Mike, she cleverly manages to arrange for the two of them to go to the ball together. She also succeeds in linking up shy Angela with Eric, as well as Lauren and Tyler.

Nevertheless, Bella's admirers aren't quite that easy to shake off. Tyler, for example, uses the occasion to get an invitation to the end of year prom. At the beginning of *Twilight* Bella had never had a boyfriend – now she has a choice of three, plus a fourth who's very attractive and mysterious.

It's worth noting how Renée, as Bella's mother, sees Bella and Edward at the beginning of the third book. She speaks shrewdly of a secret she senses between Bella and Edward. She goes on to note that Bella matches her movements to his, and that they're like a pair of magnets, or that Bella is like a satellite of Edward. Renée's comments hit the bull's-eye, although Bella feels guilty for dispelling her doubts so skilfully – the doubts of yet another person questioning the normality of her relationship with Edward.

Like the chorus of a song, the dangerous, the impossible, the forbidden elements of Bella and Edward's relationship come up again and again throughout the course of the *Twilight* saga. It begins with Edward warding off friendship and continues in countless scenes where he has to fight the temptation to give his desire for Bella free rein. Their relationship follows the patterns of mad passion. Part of the excitement in reading this series is following the many attempts to quench their driving passion.

Edward protests that her safety is more important to him than his own desires, and feels a mischievous happiness when he realises that her safety requires him to be with her round the clock. And Bella, for her part, toys with the thought that by putting herself in danger, she can force him to be there with her.

When they finally confess their love to one another, she whispers, 'I love you' and he replies simply, 'You are my life now'.

A Model Relationship

Like a sword of Damocles, impossibility overshadows Edward and Bella's relationship. It could be compared with other 'impossible' relationships – couples who, for whatever reason (age-related, aesthetic, social or religious differences, homosexuality, inter-racial relationships), don't fit the norms, and suffer the sorts of difficulties Edward and Bella experience. The difficulties Edward and Bella face will turn up time and time in the *Twilight* saga. Edward says at one point he's still waiting for the moment when one of them sees or experiences or says something the other person simply can't bear. Then that person would turn away disgusted or run off screaming. Edward wouldn't stop Bella from leaving. Quite the opposite, in a way he wishes she would, so that she could be safe. On the other hand, he longs to be by her side at all times. It's hard to decide which is best for them.

The atmosphere between them is always worse when Bella shows too clearly how obsessed she is with him. But it isn't just a question of being physically close: a multitude of reasons is shown why being together is very difficult for the two of them. They have a complex relationship of attraction and repulsion. Of closeness and distance. How often does Edward beg her to stay out of his way? How often does he suffer because he doesn't understand her, because he can't read her thoughts?

Despite being unique, the relationship between Edward and Bella can be compared in many aspects to any normal romantic relationship. Edward's inability to read Bella's thoughts leads him to ask her again and again the question people newly in love ask each other so often: what are you thinking? Bella considers herself and her life to be average and boring and she keeps silent. This means Edward has to be even more talkative. What he says sometimes sounds like a confession, but Bella reassures Edward that he shouldn't be constantly worried about upsetting or frightening her.

Bella also tries very hard to be allowed to enjoy his physical perfection. But, like an innocent teenager trying out kissing, she knows the limits; she doesn't want to put his self-control under too much strain. It's not difficult to see the metaphor here behind going too far in real-life relationships. Edward himself speaks of 'the longing – the thirst of this monster that I am' and later of other desires, which are still new to him. He's not used to feeling so human.

There's no lack of warning from people who want to protect Bella from the Cullens. Early on, for example, Mike tells Bella that her new boyfriend looks at her as though she were something good to eat. And he says that without any background knowledge. Bella, as so often in the early stages, is torn between hysterics and a cheeky giggle. Mike's comment allows the reader to stand back from Bella's point of view for a moment and imagine whether Edward really does look at Bella as a predator would its prey. Billy Black in particular warns Bella urgently against the friendship because he knows exactly what vampires can be like.

Conversely, Bella is also a controversial figure in the Cullen household. Bella and Edward's relationship is judged very differently by the various members of the family: Carlisle, Esme and Alice are the most understanding, while Rosalie is the most negative.

Bella's first visit to the Cullen house shows this dilemma clearly and forms the next step in the story of a difficult romantic partnership. Bella's afraid that the vampire family might not like her. But then she feels like she's meeting a fairy-tale character when the beautiful and thoughtful Esme, possibly her future mother-in-law, steps forward. But disaster still looms at all their meetings, although it doesn't actually take shape until, at the beginning of the second book, Jasper tries to kill her at her eighteenth birthday party, prompting the whole Cullen family to leave Forks.

Contrasting the physical danger and perfection of Edward is the down-to-earth Jacob Black, and the relationship between Bella and Jacob is quite different, but still has its own intense quality. They knew one another as children. Their fathers, Charlie and Billy, are best friends. Since they met again at the beginning of *Twilight* there has been confusion between them. Bella flirted with Jacob to get him to tell her the stories about vampires and werewolves, yet he stays close to her despite all his negative feelings about the vampires and the life she desires. In fact, his love grows stronger and more desperate until it's finally resolved in *Breaking Dawn* by Renesmee, Edward and Bella's exceptional daughter, who Jacob imprints on, thus diffusing the complicated relationship triangle.

Despite her obsession with Edward, Bella also has strong feelings for Jacob. She tries time and again to make it clear to Jacob that it is friendship and not love that she feels for him. And yet, it is such a strong friendship that Bella herself is not always clear where the boundaries between romantic love and friendship lie. After all, Bella's and Jacob's fates are intrinsically linked and during Edward's absence, which takes up most of *New Moon*, they grow very close.

Jacob is an interesting contrast to Edward, with Jacob posessing a number of appealing traits missing in Edward – from being warm-blooded to being mortal (Stephenie's werewolves can stay young for a very long time but can then get very old and die in the end). He also has a certain down-to-earth feeling about him: his old sofa in a small room, the corrugated iron workshop, warm Coke. All potentially negative aspects which, thanks to Jacob's goodness, openness and winning smile, become positive elements, which can't be overshadowed by any amount of luxury the Cullens can offer, not even their breathtakingly beautiful house. Quite the opposite: socially, Bella is far closer to her childhood friend than to the super-rich Edward.

Bella has a constant longing, a homesickness, for the simple idyll that Jacob's life represents for her, but this is severely disturbed by Jacob's sudden growing up and becoming a werewolf. *Eclipse* is marked by both the competition and the co-operation between Edward and Jacob. Bella stands between the two men, sometimes helpless, sometimes cunning. Both love her and want to protect her. They each use different methods and each sees in the other her greatest danger, and the different natures of her two admirers make life very difficult for her.

When Bella and Jacob see an eagle over the ocean in La Push, which dives down to catch a fish, Jacob starts philosophising about life and death, about the relationship between the hunter and his prey. As the eagle rises, struggling with the weight of the fish, Jacob comments that the fish never tries to kiss the eagle, referring to Bella and Edward. She responds quickly, praising the beauty of the eagle and wonders whether maybe the fish has tried. Jacob's tone grows sharper and he asks whether it's looks and the money that make the difference. His question hits a mark, since beauty and wealth really are issue-areas for her. Bella insists she would love Edward even without these qualities – despite the fact that in moments of passion she focuses on his appearance, and there are many references to Bella's feeling that the lifestyle gap between her and Edward is too great. Bella sometimes feels Edward's perfection is a burden, as strengthening her own self-doubt, but far more frequently it is her amazement at Edward's extreme qualities that makes up her fascination, passion and love for him, alongside his selflessness, his intelligence and kindness.

Can the choices we make in love really be explained though? Jacob points out that people should find a mate from within their own species. Bella dismisses this as stupid, since that would mean she'd have to be with Mike and probably marry him. The point is that Stephenie Meyer's love story lifts us out of the everyday by presenting us with a controversial supernatural ideal, leading to an intensity of feeling which a mere mortal can only dream of.

I conducted an internet-based survey to which many girls and young women responded with enthusiasm, focusing on particular aspects of the *Twilight* series. They show many interesting viewpoints, which I will share throughout the book, but here, I asked them about their opinion of Edward.

'I just think the character of Edward is really great – as do a lot of fans, I should think. Not just his perfect looks, though that's enough to ensure that you – and I really mean this – fall in love with him. He's got such a great personality as well. On the one hand he's distant and threatening, but then on the other so loving. Edward was really the reason I fell in love with the book.'

'Edward is the best thing about the novels. My teenage years may not be so far behind me (I'm 21 years old) but I felt like I'd been whisked back to being a teenager. A mysterious, handsome boy fancies the self-described ugly duckling. This woke my romantic imagination as I wasn't a very confident teenager either.'

'I'm not exactly a fan of Edward like most people are. I prefer the minor characters. I think the varied characters of the Cullen family are really interesting.'

'You have to see Edward without the rose-tinted spectacles and also be willing to recognise his weaknesses and mistakes. Girls, the guy's not perfect – way too bossy for my liking!'

'I have an extreme craving for Edward. I always want to know what he's going to do next, why he's going to do it and what he's thinking and feeling when he does it.'

'Do I ever have erotic thoughts about being with Edward? Yes, why ever not? Edward's described as desirable. That kind of thinking is to be expected. I should think most female readers think about what it would be like to have a relationship with Edward.'

'Well, be honest, who wouldn't want a man like Edward Cullen?'

'What gives Edward his particular charm is that he's from a different era, when that type of charm was standard. I think that's a big part of who Edward is and for that reason I don't think a boy like Edward could exist now. Additionally, I have to agree with Robert Pattinson – he points out that Edward is always described as being perfect. At first I also thought it was just all coming through Bella's thoughts, she's in love with him and so sees everything through rose-tinted glasses, but since reading some of *Midnight Sun*, Edward really does seem totally perfect (which I find a bit disturbing) and I don't think that anyone can be perfect.'

'Edward is the perfect gentleman (yes, women do like that kind of thing!), not a mean macho man, who grabs himself one pretty girl after another. He had a rebellious phase but in the end he realised that wasn't for him and spends his time on meaningful occupations. He's really the epitome of virtue and values. Mind you, it's as a vampire that he's so perfect. As a "normal" man he wouldn't be half so nice, because the really great thing is that he develops these feelings as a direct result of his "un-normality".'

I also asked them how they responded to Bella's character.

'In my memory, Bella's a clumsy girl who keeps getting into difficult situations and I think that describes myself pretty well, too. Apart from that I could see from her thought processes that she kept asking herself why Edward fell in love with her – after all, she thinks she's not at all pretty. That's like me too. I don't think I'm very pretty either and I would never imagine that a perfect man like Edward could fall in love with me.'

'I think every girl can identify with Bella one way or another. Her clumsiness, her independence, her simple way of being, her common sense – a normal girl, in short.'

'I can really identify with Bella, that wave of first love is just huge. And the way she wants to give everything up for him, and is even willing to die for him.'

'Bella isn't really a typical teenager. She seems very grown up, is even described like this by her rather chaotic mother and cares a lot about other people's wellbeing. Whatever she does, she thinks first of her father, Charlie; she usually sticks to the rules, mostly without argument. She's really more "housewife" than rebel. Sometimes I think it's scary how grown up she is, how caring she is about her whole family and friends.'

'Pretty much the only thing I have in common with Bella is clumsiness . . . I can't walk ten steps without bumping into something or tripping over. Other than that, I can identify much better with Alice. But I can still put myself in Bella's shoes, which is mainly due to the author's empathetic style.'

'From book three onwards she did get on my nerves rather a lot and I didn't really understand her, but in general, naturally, I can see a number of parallels between us. Clumsiness seems to be fairly common and I'm no exception. Although I do manage to get through a fair number of days without serious injury, unlike Bella. I don't have lots and lots of friends either (but the ones I've got are great) and I was never one of the popular kids when I was at school. The fact that she's got a lot of love to give, and saves this for people it's worth investing those feelings and emotions in, is something I see in myself as well. I could also really understand the emptiness and lethargy she felt in book two, because of Edward being gone.'

'Bella is brave. After all, she dares to get together with a vampire and she's not scared of him or what could happen.'

'I feel what she's feeling when I read the book and get a funny feeling in my tummy whenever the name Edward Cullen is mentioned.'

'I think I have character traits similar to Bella as well, like her persistence and the way she wants to "sacrifice" herself for others, even if it's just a test in a French lesson.'

'I can only understand Bella to a certain extent. I think I'd have managed things a bit differently if my boyfriend had left me. And I think I wouldn't have accepted it so easily if he just came back again.'

'Sometimes she exaggerates, like I wouldn't leap off a cliff for a (normal) boy, well maybe for Edward. But overall I think the way she behaves is only OK.'

'If I were Bella, I'd have done a few things differently. Obviously I understand her. She loves Edward more than anything and tries to bind him to her as tightly as possible. But she makes a lot of mistakes. Especially with Jacob. It was hard to read about how she behaves towards him. She wants to set boundaries, but isn't really honest with him. So it's understandable that he thinks he has a chance with her.'

About half the fans, for whatever reason, felt they could only partly identify with Bella. This seems to be partly due to the controversy over Bella's relative liberation as a female. Is she or is she not liberated?

'I know Stephenie Meyer's a Mormon and that's why I get her way of writing. Mormons believe women have an inferior position to men – they'd really like the woman to be in the kitchen while the man goes to work, just like it was in traditional olden-day families, so I can understand why Stephenie Meyer gave Bella an inferior role next to Edward. A role in which the woman sacrifices herself for her beloved man.'

'The achievement of feminism should be that every woman is allowed to choose her own path, which Bella achieves. Only the pregnancy described in the fourth book reminded me of the traditional female role: the weak woman must have children and be eternally grateful to the strong man who rescues her!'

'Bella's quite simply daring, courageous and eternally in love.'

'Bella's fighting for love and, in that situation, you just have to give some things up.'

'I think if you're perfectly and one hundred per cent sure of what you're doing and just as sure of your partner, then nothing's too much to sacrifice. And that's exactly what she does, she makes a decision, is one hundred per cent sure of herself and gives up even her life for her true love. No one could give more.'

'Edward is exactly what Bella wants. She knows the price and she pays it. I don't think that she can be called anti-feminist which, I think, would mean she'd been forced, by society or other people, into a decision without being able to choose for herself. But Bella does have a choice and there are sections in the books where we see her weighing up various alternatives and finally making a decision that is sensible for her. To me that's what maturity and liberation is, weighing up possibilities and then making the best decision for yourself, even if that goes against all the rules of society.'

'I don't think that sacrificing yourself for love is anti-feminist at all.'

'Everything's different with Bella and Edward. I don't see Bella as an anti-feminist heroine; she's just a girl who's finally found her place in the world and her ultimate true love, which is probably what everybody would wish for. Bella herself is a strong character. She isn't just in the shadow of the Cullens.'

'What she does, she does for the good of others, acting out of passion and love. Of course, it can look like she's just a classic "women belong in the kitchen" character, but to me that's an expression of how grown up she is. She could have been described as the "All-American-Girl", but that's just what she's not. She can't dance, isn't interested in fashion or her own appearance, isn't sporty and doesn't like shopping. Her self-sacrificing attitude isn't restricted to Edward. She'd do anything for any member of her family.'

'I couldn't believe my eyes when a load of "women's libbers" got so worked up when *Breaking Dawn* was published. According to them the book was sending out the wrong message, namely: give up on education, marry young (preferably a rich bloke), get pregnant quickly and be a kept woman. Huh? It's a book. Everybody's free to choose their own path.'

'I was shocked when I read the claims that Bella isn't liberated! She's a woman who's found the love of her life – or probably even more than that! And for me it was a clear and essential part of the story that she gave so much – but in the end gets so much back in return! And the fact that Edward rescues her really can't be called anti-feminist! He loves her just as much as she loves him. I thought it obvious that he would use his attributes to rescue her from anything and anyone! I think anyone who describes the character of Bella as being anti-feminist has misunderstood a large part of the saga.'

'On the one hand Bella makes her decisions independently; she wasn't brought up to act the way she decides to in the end, nor is she pushed into it – this behaviour must be seen in a positive light. But I still think Bella lets Edward get away with too much. He confines her movements, he makes decisions for her, forbids her to spend time with her best friend and she responds to all this with hardly a complaint. On the other hand, you have to remember that she's very young and inexperienced. It's her first big love affair and lots of young girls would behave in exactly the same way: they easily give themselves up for their partner. Giving up her old life can, I think, only partially be seen as a sacrifice since this very sacrifice opens new doors for her. Although it could be seen that in the fourth book she chooses "a kid over a career", as a vampire she's got all the time in the world to get a really good university education and to make something of herself!'

For many people, it wasn't just the characters so much as the love they share that made the books so appealing.

'It's Bella's "great love" for Edward; but also his uncertainty and anxiety in relation to her; his deep melancholy leading him to question everything but still not resisting this deep love, allowing it; you can feel his love grow.'

'It's a beautiful love story, coupled with myths and legends about vampires – and exciting too.'

'My favourite bit (of course) is the relationship between Edward and Bella. In the first book I really felt for them, wondering when they would finally get it together.'

'The theme of romantic young love against all the odds and despite common sense.'

'Once you've had enough of the fantasy level, there's a whole other intensity of love you can really feel.'

'Their love doesn't seem to have a chance, but you feel for them and hope they'll get their happy ending. Just like Shakespeare's *Romeo and Juliet*. You want to believe in this love, believe it's real. It's the impossibility of their situation. They know they can't live without each other ever again. And the reader knows as well that it doesn't matter how hard they try to stay apart their longing will just keep growing.'

✦

THE TWILIGHT VAMPIRE

A WHOLE NEW BREED

It is Jacob Black who is the first to introduce the subject of werewolves and vampires to Bella and the reader. The story is cleverly set up so that Jacob himself believes he's telling ghost stories, although it's already obvious to the reader that he is in fact telling the (literary) truth. Stephenie Meyer is playing a fabulous game with different levels of reality.

It all begins with legends from the time of the Flood: the ancient Quileute – Jacob's tribe – it is said, took their canoes to the top of the mountain and tied them to the tops of the tallest trees and in this way they survived, like Noah and his Ark. Another legend says that the Quileute are descended from wolves and that they are still their brothers. That's why tribal law forbids the killing of wolves. Stories about the 'cold ones' also come from the same time as the wolf legends, although there are some newer stories too, so Jacob tells an amazed Bella. She finds out that Jacob's great-grandfather, a tribal elder, is supposed to have actually known some of the cold ones. He made a treaty with them, according to which they are to stay off Quileute land and harm no one, or face the consequences.

The cold ones are the natural and only enemies of the Quileute shapeshifters who phase into wolf or human at will. It's not until *Breaking Dawn* that Bella finds out that the Quileute didn't have to become wolves – they could have shapeshifted into any animal.

The clan of cold ones, which lived near the La Push territories at the time of Jacob's great-grandfather behaved differently to previous cold ones. They hunted and fed on animals and didn't pose any threat to the Quileute, which was why a truce was reached. The cold ones promised not to attack the Quileute and in return the tribe promised not to betray the clan to the pale-faces. The Quileute had the impression this clan of cold ones was civilised. But they were still afraid they might present some danger. No one could know whether they might get too hungry to resist their nature.

Soon it is clear that the clan in question was indeed the Cullen family. Even then, their leader was Carlisle. By the time Bella's 'people' – the pale-faces – arrived, however, the Cullen clan had already disappeared. People, clan, tribe, pale-faces, territory, Native Americans, and superstitions – the very choice of words whisks the reader into a wild world in which legends were taken more seriously than they are now.

In the end, though, Bella does exactly what many readers

would probably do too. She goes to her computer and enters 'vampire' into an internet search engine. And readers will find – if they choose to check it – that just as when she did, a list of the oddest vampire websites will appear.

A SENSE OF RIGHT AND WRONG

When Bella starts trying to understand vampires, she begins with Montague Summer's definition and Rousseau's reflections on the existence of vampires. She also looks at the contrast between legends – in which there are only very few of the Dracula type – and films, more often than not, variations on Bram Stoker's bloodsucker myth. Bella, however, is on a hunt for deviations from the traditional sort of vampire and studies the various vampire myths from across the world quite objectively. Bella interprets the legends of demonic, beautiful women and their child victims as simply being an explanation of high infant mortality. Bella's interpretation is more than likely, and it's a thought worth pursuing that the Cullens and the Blacks might also be an explanation for something else. Does Stephenie's vampire and werewolf universe have functions over and beyond mere entertainment? Is there something hidden in this passionate and exciting story, something not quite so easy to spot?

But Bella can't find many parallels between the myths she reads about and the Cullens. The Romanian 'Varacolaci', an undead being, who appears as a 'beautiful, pale-skinned human'; the Slovakian 'Nelapsi', who was strong and fast; and the Italian 'Stregoni benefici', a good vampire and an enemy to all evil vampires. This is what Bella pins her hopes on. And this was indeed the basis for Stephenie's *Twilight* myth. She adapted it and developed it so far away from the original elements, that in the end a *Twilight* universe was born – and an entirely new breed of vampire.

Characteristics of a Twilight Vampire

- Fast
- Strong
- Beautiful
- Cold skin
- Pale
- Stays out of sunlight (though out of choice for not being seen as something different, rather than the more traditional causing pain or death)
- Changing eye colour – red, black or gold
- Sleepless
- Breathless (literally: they don't actually need to breathe, they do so out of habit and can hold their breath as long as they want to, they just can't smell anything while not breathing)
- Immortal (unless they are torn apart and burned)
- Blood drinkers (animal blood only for the Cullens)
- Enemies of the werewolf
- Special powers – many *Twilight* vampires have enhanced qualities of their human selves, giving them individual special powers, like Edward's reading of minds, Bella's protection of

minds, Alice's reading of the future and Jasper's manipulation of feelings.

The Cullens

The Cullens also have a unique style when it comes to feeding – they hunt when they feel like it, but they can 'fill up' on blood which enables them to live peaceably among humans without falling into temptation for some time. The Cullens call themselves vegetarians, a family joke. Hunting animals doesn't completely quench their thirst, but gives enough strength – usually – to resist hunting humans, to not be monsters.

The driving force behind the existence of this new breed of vampire was Carlisle's strong sense of right and wrong (and of course Stephenie's): why does Edward and all the other Cullens go against their own nature? Most vampires, even the Volturi, are content to be the way they are. The more intelligent of them, however, are curious to understand why the Cullens choose to abstain from human blood, to live as 'vegetarians'.

In Edward's view, nobody has to just accept the cards destiny deals them. He strives to rise above his fate and stretch the horizons of his existence. He wants to maintain his human sensitivities, the morally good ones, however weakened they may seem.

Finding Yourself

The Cullens' attitudes to humans are as varied as the types of relationship it's possible to have with another person. Jasper was the last to join the Cullen family and he finds abstinence from human blood very hard.

Emmett has been abstaining for a long time. He has fallen in love twice before in the way Edward has now. 'Even the strongest of us fall off the wagon', Edward explains. Bella and the reader can guess what this means. That's why she asks Edward whether a bitter end is unavoidable, and is surprised at how calmly and easily she can talk about her own death. Sometimes Edward assures her it's possible, at other times he doesn't quite believe it himself, which is what leads to the break in *New Moon*, when he leaves Bella. When he first saw Bella, he saw her as a demon come to ruin him. After much going back and forth on the matter, after countless murderous thoughts, after fleeing to Alaska, after mature consideration, after strengthening his self-discipline, he finally admits his love to her in the clearing: she's now the most important thing in his life. But even this admission isn't a guarantee of an eternal and safe life together. Love and death are always close neighbours. Together they laugh at the 'idiocy and the sheer impossibility of such a moment', a moment when the lion confesses his love to the lamb.

Edward emphasises that he does have human instincts, even if they're buried deeply. He compares his thirst for blood with an alcoholic's thirst and uses this metaphor again to explain Bella's unique scent to her. His fixation on Bella is like an alcoholic's passion for a fine cognac. That expensive drink would smell quite different to everything else, for example to stale beer. But then Edward decides that the comparison with alcohol is too weak and speaks of a drug addiction instead. Surprised, Bella wants to know whether she's his favourite type of drug and Edward answers that she doesn't just smell like his favourite kind of drug, she is exactly his drug.

A fundamental characteristic of the Cullen strain of vampire is the so-called rescuing of dying humans. It's a particularly difficult process. Only a few of the Cullens have the necessary self-control to carry it out – and it's extremely painful for the person being changed.

Carlisle was the first to put this form of rescue into practice and with that he laid the foundation stone of the new Cullen vampire. He did it out of loneliness and against the backdrop of his very particular biography. Born the son of a pastor in London in the late Middle Ages, Carlisle personally experienced hordes of uncivilised undead. His father led numerous witch-hunts and Carlisle followed in his footsteps and he proved himself very skilful. He didn't see demons where there weren't any, but he was persistent and discovered a coven of real vampires. They were living in the city sewers and only hunted at night. An ancient vampire, speaking Latin and probably weak with hunger, smelled the mob and fled, but Carlisle pursued him. However, the old vampire – Edward calls him 'the creature' – was too hungry: he attacked Carlisle. Carlisle knew that anything which had come into contact with the monster would be destroyed by the humans, so he tried to save his own life and hid in a cellar – in agony for three days.

Once he'd realised what he'd become, he tried to kill himself –
he threw himself from houses and bridges, drowned himself in
the sea – all without success. Carlisle was strong and resisted
his thirst, revolted by his craving, and was filled with self-
hatred and wanted to starve himself to death. But even that
was not possible. In the end, he attacked some deer, got his
strength back and saw animals as a solution. After all, he'd
eaten game in his old life. He developed his new philosophy
from this experience: it seemed possible to exist without being
a monster, without killing humans, without creating even more
monsters. By living like this, he wanted to find himself again.

Targeted Transformation

As a human, Carlisle had always been intelligent and keen to
learn – now he had unlimited time at his disposal. As he studied
at universities throughout Europe, he met others of his kind,
who were far more educated and civilised than the monsters in
London's sewers; cultivated vampires with nice manners, yet all
of them fed on a conventional diet of humans, considering it the
natural way of life for vampires and couldn't understand
Carlisle's way of thinking. He spent a few decades with the
much older and highly educated Volturi, but wasn't able to
convert them to his humanistic approach. He dreamed of a
different way of life, of a community of like-minded vampires
and directed his hope towards the New World. In America, he
hoped to find others like himself, but he found instead that
witches, werewolves and vampires were more and more

becoming figures of legend and fairy-tales. He also, however, saw how some 'monsters' were able to live amongst unsuspecting humans as one of them. He tried to do this too, but remained lonely. During the flu epidemic in the early twentieth century, he was working night shifts in a Chicago hospital. What happened next is told twice, briefly and curtly in book one, then more fully and gently in book two. At first Bella hears that Carlisle wanted to create a companion for himself. Since he didn't quite know how he himself was transformed, he was still hesitant. He absolutely didn't want to take anybody's life the way the old vampire had taken his. Then he found Edward, who, along with other dying patients, was on a ward for hopeless cases. Carlisle had nursed Edward's parents, so knew that Edward had no other relations once they died. In book two Edward's mother plays a larger role. As if in the face of death she could sense Carlisle's supernatural powers, she used all her remaining strength to command Carlisle to save her son Edward – at any price. For Carlisle that was the permission he needed.

Carlisle's theory about the talents – the individual powers many vampires possess – claims that they bring the strongest abilities they had as humans with them into their vampire existence, where they are intensified. So Edward was already sensitive to what people around him were thinking. Alice already had precognitive facilities. Carlisle brought great compassion, Esme the ability to love passionately, Rosalie brought tenacity and Jasper always had a charismatic nature, getting others to see things his way.

Carlisle is also the founder of one of the most important characteristics of the new vampire ethos: targeted and deliberate transformation – Carlisle will only change a person who's dying anyway and would never change anybody into a vampire who had another option. Carlisle's thoughtfulness and kindness is the foundation on which the Cullens have built their conscience. So the Cullens' motto is the same as Stephenie's: no one's perfect, we all make mistakes but we can learn from them and make the best of ourselves.

THANKS TO LOVE

There aren't many vampires like the Cullens, who live unrecognised amongst humans. Only very few live settled lives. Only those vampires who have given up hunting humans are able to live any amount of time amongst them. Until book three, the Cullens only know one other family like them, living a settled life in a village in Alaska. Most of the other vampires they know are nomads, living in the North. They're ordinary vampires, and therefore evil.

When the three vampires, Laurent, James and Victoria step into the clearing towards the end of *Twilight*, disturbing the Cullens' baseball game, Bella compares their respectful manner with that of predators meeting a larger and unknown group of their own kind. She stresses their cat-like gait, as though they were constantly on the point of crouching. They are dressed like backpackers, except they are barefoot and their clothes are tattered.

Like all predators, *Twilight* vampires are equipped with more than enough abilities like physical strength, invulnerability, speed, sharpened senses and additional perceptive faculties. And, of course, vampires are unbelievably patient. Precisely how patient they can be is very apparent in the hotel scene in Phoenix, when Alice and Jasper, in their hiding place supposedly safe from James, remain absolutely calm – unlike Bella, who is anything other than calm. Understandably, immortality and endless patience seem to go together.

Vampires are also attractive to their prey, much like carnivorous plants, and are poisonous. Like snakes, their venom comes out of their teeth, but it doesn't kill, it incapacitates. It spreads through the bloodstream and causes pain so great the victim is unable to run away.

If the person isn't killed outright by the vampire, and the poison is allowed to spread unchecked, they will be changed into a vampire themselves within a few days. The precise length of time depends on where the victim is bitten – the nearer the heart, the quicker the change – and on the concentration of poison in the blood. The transformation is extremely painful from start to finish, with the victim wishing they were dead. When the heart stops beating, the change is complete. For all vampires, the pain of changing is the clearest memory of their human life.

Vampires are a little like sharks. As soon as they have smelled or tasted blood they can't stop drinking. Which is why controlled changes, like the ones Carlisle does, are so difficult to do. They demand the utmost willpower of both parties. The vampire has to have enough self-control to bite and not drink and the victim has to endure the agony.

COMPANY OF WOLVES

Stephenie doesn't only create a new breed of vampires, but also a new breed of werewolves. The Quileute tribal elders say the tribe always had magical power, at first not the magic of transformation but of spirit warriors. Like in Ovid's *Metamorphoses* and later in *The Matrix*, they were able to separate their mind from their body, a technique they refined over generations. When one of the warriors was in dire need, he asked a wolf to allow him space and let him share his body, and this is how the *Twilight* werewolves came into existence.

When Ephraim Black and Carlisle Cullen agree a peace treaty, the Cullens swear no vampire will harm a human, including feeding from or changing a person. But this treaty is constantly under threat from nomad vampires thirsting for revenge and from Bella's jealous admirers – Edward and Jacob. Who has broken the treaty? Edward, who plans to change Bella? Or Jacob, who told Bella about the existence of vampires in the first place?

The Quileute can live many generations without any tribe members transforming into wolves, but pass on the genetic ability to do so. The werewolves only return when vampires return.

Changing from human into wolf form is mostly an instinctive reaction and hard to predict, but can be controlled with willpower, and done on demand. The moment of change from one form into the other is hard to understand, it's as though they lose their identity for a moment. This makes it difficult for Alice to predict their future.

At the beginning of *New Moon*, Jacob already hints at cooperation between werewolves and vampires. When Victoria reappears around Forks, it would have been possible to catch her if they'd made a collaborative effort, but their rapprochement takes place instead slowly, and in lots of small steps.

In contrast to the vampires, Jacob maintains that he's still human. What he is, he says, was born within him, is part of who he is, part of his family, part of his tribe. Quil is happy to be part of the pack. He thinks it's cool to be a werewolf. The others are less than happy when they find out about their other nature. But most of them get used to it: freedom, strength, and the feeling of belonging to a very special family.

One of the physical peculiarities of these werewolves is that when they're in human form, their whole body is much warmer than normal body temperature, as though they are running a constant fever.

Even more important is their unusual way of ageing. A Quileute child doesn't know whether he's destined to become a werewolf. He grows up thinking all the myths and legends about werewolves must be invented stories. When the situation arises, when there are vampires around, the werewolf gene in the Quileute is activated and within a few months a pubescent boy becomes fully developed. That's why at seventeen, when *Eclipse* begins, Jacob is, in biological terms, actually about twenty-five years old.

Just like the vampires, the werewolves are bound to keep their secret. Nobody is allowed to find out about their true existence. A very few exceptions, like the council of elders, prove the rule.

Communication between the wolves is also novel. In wolf form, and only in wolf form, they can hear the other werewolves' thoughts. The disadvantages are that there's no private life and no secrets from the others, which can be embarrassing. But during a battle, for example, this can be to their advantage; they can send warnings to each other and discuss strategy during the fight. These werewolves also heal from wounds and injuries very quickly, even those suffered in human form.

What's so special about Stephenie's vampires and werewolves is their relationships with each other and, of course, as the saga progresses, their ability to form friendships. She invests both creatures with a sense of right and wrong, which is traditionally absent from them, suggesting her belief that everyone has a sense of right and wrong.

When I spoke to fans about vampires, a surprising number of them said they believed that vampires exist. Here are their thoughts on the matter.

'I'm fifteen and quite a big fan of vampires and vampire stories and other similar stuff, but I still don't believe vampires exist.'

'To be honest, since reading these books I could believe anything.'

'Bloodsucking monsters from kids' stories? No, I don't believe in them. The *Twilight* vampires? I'm not quite so sure about that.'

'Yes, I believe vampires exist, or at least vampire-like creatures, why else would there be so many myths and stories? They must have some kind of real background.'

'I'd be really happy if there were vampires like the Cullens. I'd want Edward to bite me! But it could be true that there are vampires and we just don't notice because they've got used to humans and drink other blood, like the Cullens do. It's really pretty much the same question as whether there are aliens.'

'It's a difficult question. Vampire myths first appeared when rabies was raging in Europe, the symptoms of which include some of the signs of today's vampires, like light sensitivity, although there's controversy there too. Apart from that, there are some diseases or deformities which can also look like the features of vampires, like prominent teeth. It's quite usual for society to explain things that are either difficult or impossible to understand with mythical creatures or legends.'

'Yes, I believe in vampires! That is, I believe in Stephenie Meyer's vampires. I don't think the Cullens really exist (it would be nice if they did), but I do think that there are vampires living somewhere in the world. Not the bloodthirsty and violent ones, but the civilised kind.'

'I don't believe they exist in this world. Although I have to say, characters in my fantasy world sometimes seem too realistic to be just invented. But no, they don't actually exist.'

'There really are girls who leave their window open at night, just in case Edward decides to climb in, but personally I don't believe in vampires.'

'Well, I've never met one. But I also think: never say never. People used to believe in vampires and I can't imagine that all those stories are just made up. I can't imagine that they do exist, but by the same token, I can't be sure that they don't exist.'

'It would be nice if they existed. But we would probably have noticed them by now!'

Lots of people think life as a vampire would be hard to bear.

'I think the idea of being immortal, never being able to sleep and only ever being able to stay in any one place for a few years is more frightening than anything else. It's impossible for the Cullens to build relationships with other people, or rather only with like-minded vampires. There's so much vampires have to do without. Of course, there's no doubt there are many things that make a vampire life attractive, but in my opinion these are outweighed by the literally horrifying aspects that I couldn't live with. And anyway, I hate pain and would never survive the transformation's three days of feeling like you're on fire.'

'On the one hand it sounds interesting, you can "experience" a lot over the years, on the other hand you'd keep losing friends who weren't immortal, that would mean always having to say goodbye a lot. Eternity's an unimaginable amount of time.'

But lots of people dream of having vampire powers.

'To be immortal does have its attractions. You might experience the future you dreamed of, just the way you imagined it, or it might be completely different. What's going to happen to the earth, if the theories about the "end of the world" are really true, and just generally how the world and we humans will develop in the future. I'd really like to be immortal and I'd also like to live in a family like the Cullens, because their secret really binds them together even more closely.'

'I've always wanted to become a vampire. As mad as that sounds. And living in the Cullen family would probably be very exciting. Emmett's crude jokes, Esme and Carlisle's loving care.

Who wouldn't want a family like that? They stick together. They're there for each other. I would love to be taken in by their family.'

'It would be really great to be immortal, I think, and living with the Cullens would be nice too, but only if my own family were nearby and immortal too. Why would I want to be immortal if my family and friends weren't?'

'I'd rather be part of a werewolf family!'

'Be part of the Cullen family? I wouldn't have a problem with that :-) I think twenty-four hours in a day is a bit short since you sleep through a large part of it. Of course, the strength, speed and beauty are also quite tempting (most people are a little superficial). Mind you, I would also prefer the "vegetarian" diet.'

An
international
Bestseller

I love debut novels. Authors tend to write their first book without haste or pressure, without expectation or advance payment and without any idea at all as to whether their text will ever be printed, published or read by strangers. This freedom and light-heartedness while writing has a positive effect on the text an author writes. What's special about Stephenie is that even once the first book was done, her imagination, intensity and her lightness of touch remained.

With only a few exceptions, all the early professional readers of the first manuscript felt the potential in Stephenie's work. From the outset, Stephenie's agent and publisher set up an intensive marketing strategy to accompany the book release. Young fans were spoiled with merchandising items and events. Now, in addition to calendars, bookmarks, cards and board games, there are also T-shirts, posters, Bella and Edward dolls as well as jewellery (like Bella's bracelet from Jacob and engagement ring from Edward). There's no limit to the merchandisers' imagination: currently a range of *Twilight* perfumes, each based on a main character, are selling like hot cakes.

Even before the first book was published, the internet was functioning as the most important tool in the spread of *Twilight* fever. There were countless official and unofficial websites across the world where fans were exchanging ideas, rumours were started, facts were listed and stories told. Stephenie herself contributes to the proliferation of information about the *Twilight* saga, by giving explanations of her stories in many interviews and FAQs. Some of them do in fact contain inconsistencies, but she should be forgiven – when inventing new creatures, some design faults are pretty much unavoidable. She herself constantly emphasises that her stories are fictional: nothing she's invented is possible. Within her created world, however, she does try hard to remain logical. It's worth trawling through the countless *Twilight* interpretations and explanations – from the official sites to the alternative ones to explore all the possibilities.

There's an increasing amount of fan fiction on *Twilight* sites, rumours about illegally released manuscripts as well as gossip of every possible sort, which curious webmasters then circulate further. Before new books were published, contents lists were circulated a million times over, with and without spoilers. The disguised nature of the spoilers are themselves becoming more and more imaginative – sometimes in code, or mirror writing or with the background and text colour the same, so that the text is only visible once it's been highlighted – just a few things which show the imagination with which fans indulge their passion on the net.

Things get particularly heated on the internet when someone posts a bad review, a frequent occurrence in respect of *Breaking Dawn*. Here are some particularly impassioned arguments that come up quite often.

'Stephenie Meyer blatantly breaks the rules of her vampire world that she herself set out on the internet. Certain sites proclaimed that vampire poison replaced all body fluids (an answer given by Stephenie Meyer in an interview). Since *Breaking Dawn*, it's suddenly become "almost all body fluids".'

'Average human growth + non-growth as a vampire = super fast growth. Wouldn't it be more logical to think that: average human growth + non-growth of vampire = slowed growth?'

'Bella's change and time as a newborn doesn't seem right – Bella, who's always complaining, manages to get through three days of hell's fires, lying quite still and without making a single sound? And then has instant self-control?

'Bella's change should also have been something really special. Wasn't the whole point that she was giving her life up voluntarily in order to be with Edward? Instead there's another situation in which Bella has to be rescued by Edward, making her change no different to Edward's, Esme's, Rosalie's and Emmett's.'

'The birth in *Breaking Dawn*. If anyone has children of (let's say) thirteen or younger, and those children want to read this book, it's advisable to take them to one side before they begin and be sure you've explained the process of a "normal" pregnancy, a "normal" birth and a "normal" caesarean section!

Perhaps they could also be told that it's not quite the done thing to tell your husband/boyfriend you're happy to change your entire life plans if he'll just sleep with you one more time.'

'How come Carlisle, a practising doctor, and Edward, a husband with two medical degrees, need the advice of Jacob, a high school student, to come up with the idea that the tiny, developing half-vampire might just possibly prefer blood to normal human food?'

'The werewolves are revealed to actually be shapeshifters. Why was this only mentioned in the last book, and how come Edward knew this all along, but didn't think it was necessary to mention it?'

'Stephenie Meyer emphasised again and again that the whole story is supposed to be about making decisions and then Jacob imprints on Nessie and any kind of decision making goes right out the window.'

'After her change, Bella's physically perfect – where's her baby belly? Strictly speaking, it shouldn't be able to disappear, since, according to Stephenie Meyer, vampires look the way they did when they were changed forever.'

It doesn't require much imagination to guess how strongly many fans react to these criticisms, which they consider undeserved. There are some biting remarks in return and it's not exaggeration to speak of a generally cutting atmosphere in many forums, particularly in view of the controversy surrounding *Breaking Dawn*. The sites are riddled with pros and cons and on her homepage Stephenie herself skilfully defuses most of these, including many of the accusations and doubts listed above. The gripe remains though that the questions should be answerable simply from having read the books, without outside help, or, ideally, there shouldn't have been any questions at all.

Divided Opinions

Breaking Dawn isn't the first of the books to raise the odd question. Aside from the Cullens' supernatural powers, there are a number of aspects of vampire existence which the saga either hardly deals with or doesn't deal with at all. Questions about their anatomy and daily practicalities: Edward's bluish veins are visible under his skin. The fact that for decades no blood has flowed through these veins is easily explained by feeding and vampire poison.

This is also important in *Breaking Dawn* when the question of reproduction is raised. Why haven't the Cullens reproduced in the hundreds of years of their existence? Yes, vampire women can't have babies, but Emmett speaks of beguiling humans ('*la tua cantante*'). Also, we know that there aren't any beds in the Cullen bedrooms, but what about the toilets? Have they been converted, or are they just unused?

When the Cullens play baseball, a reader might well wonder what material could the ball possibly be made of that the sound of the bat hitting it is like a clap of thunder.

Would it not be hugely tempting for a vampire to use their supernatural strength to play the hero among humans, like superheroes and villains intervening in daily life?

The people around Bella frequently come into contact with the Cullens, like during the wedding preparations. How can it be that people never wonder about their coldness or their chronic pallor? How can Carlisle Cullen work in a clinic, surrounded by trained doctors, without anyone noticing anything odd about him? This problem crops up in the film too. Edward's cold hands are mentioned a number of times, but when Carlisle is shown shaking hands with someone, nothing at all is said. Even in daily life at school it would be impossible for the Cullens to completely avoid all contact with humans, but the text avoids any such situation. Over the course of the *Twilight* saga, vampires and werewolves grow ever closer to each other. A simple handshake, the touch of an overheated werewolf hand on a super-cooled vampire hand ought to cause some kind of obvious reaction.

Rosalie's story makes the reader wonder what happened to

the people from her time. How is Vera, Rosalie's best friend in the 1930s? How are Vera's children and her husband, the carpenter? For a short time, Rosalie was jealous of Vera's happiness in her simple family life. What would be more natural than to find out how she is, how her life turned out?

Hair-splitting fans have found many more problematic areas. Some questions can be answered directly from the books, some others are answered in Stephenie's interviews. And if any doubts still remain after this, then there's always Stephenie's mantra: 'It's fun.'

But if some comments deal blows, at least as many hand out kisses – even about the controversial *Breaking Dawn*. Here's an example of a response showing qualified approval of *Breaking Dawn*:

'The worst of it is that most of the criticism is justified. The novel has several weaknesses, above all the implausible and sudden changes in the main characters, e.g. Edward, and Jacob in particular, is unrecognisable (at least he doesn't seem to be so unpleasant or grating any more). Charlie's role and his character have also been considerably changed (and Charlie with all his faults was so gloriously realistic). Looking back, I don't like the terribly reactionary (I assume very Mormon) message of the story: girls marry young and as virgins, sacrifice their lives to their families, give up on a university education and a career and live happily ever after.

'But sadly, none of this changes anything: these and the

many other weaknesses in the story didn't stop me one little bit from enjoying it, in fact I didn't even notice the problems as I read, and even looking back and in spite of all justifiable criticism, I still really like it.

'Perhaps it's because, from the beginning of the book, the plot was surprising. It developed quite differently to how I expected. It was also quite different to what I expected from the author, given the two – rather mediocre and somewhat predictable – preceding books. The plot alone (however absurd and illogical it seems in retrospect) kept me going so that I could only put the book down for a short sleep.

'Anyway, the last third of the book really was good, exciting, imaginative and surprising – a worthy end, which, to me, made up for the many annoyances of the preceding books.'

And as another example, there is also the reminder that the whole thing is about pleasure, not science.

'I think the book's good. Full stop. I really don't understand people who write such devastating critiques of serial novels. Of course the fourth book is different to its predecessors. I have to say, I was really impressed that the plot was still surprising. I hadn't read anything about it before reading it, I wanted to make my own mind up first. And I'm shocked at how much negative criticism there's been. I had thought a lot about what might happen in this book and really wondered whether the remaining 'open' elements (wedding, Bella as a vampire) could really provide enough material for a plot. And that's why I think it's so great that a completely new aspect to the story has been brought in, one I totally wasn't expecting.That's how it should be. I don't want to read a second version of a preceding book, I want to read a new one! Why can't it be judged as such? The story's the most important thing!

It's obvious every character isn't going to be described in full all over again. Why should they be? We already know and love them, just as they are. I did wonder whether I wanted such a total happy ending. It's really too much of a cliché. But I came to the conclusion that following on from the first three books, it's firstly consistent and, secondly, I'm not sure I could have believed it any other way. Or even wanted it any other way. This way at least I have closure on the story. And, let's be honest here . . . we're all happy it ended so well for everybody. And as to its message? I doubt very much that Stephenie Meyer was trying to get over any particular message, even less likely any kind of demand. It's light fiction, designed to entertain and it does that very well! And if there's any kind of message to be taken from the book, for me it's how strong and all-embracing and forgiving love can be.

Like the three preceding books, this book has managed the single most important thing: it captured my imagination, moved me emotionally and made me feel for the characters. What else could I ask of a book?'

Virtual Twilight

So internet chatter developed a life of its own and increases in intensity each time a book or film is released. There are some specific sites where fans can gather to do this and I asked the creators of a *Twilight* site about the phenomenon.

Angela is a fully trained teacher who sees *Twilight* as good material for encouraging children in the classroom to develop an enthusiasm for books. Isabella is a student studying social science. There's a sense of commitment apparent in these two women's comments, which reading the *Twilight* saga seems to bring out in many of those who run websites. It's also clear how much that increases both the enjoyment of reading and familiarity with the *Twilight* saga.

Is running the website a lot of work or is it a lot of fun too?

Isabella

'Of course it's a lot of work. The beginning was particularly hard, when we had to fill the pages and make sure there wasn't anything important missing. It's still not totally complete and we're always trying to make the pages even more informative. But its even more fun than it is hard work. Sometimes I spend all day working on the site, writing text, looking for news and trying out ideas. When I'm doing that, it's easy to forget "more important" things, like uni work. Luckily, I have quite a bit of time, which I can organise however I want so I can get everything done. Also, the rest of the team are always happy to help, which makes everything much easier!

'I'm always working on it or researching for the site, for example looking through newspapers (keeping an eye out for articles or scraps about the *Twilight* series or films). Naturally there's always the sheer fun of it to keep you going. Sometimes when I'm lying in bed at night something will occur to me, something we could add to the site or a way to improve it. When that happens, I have to get up and at least write the idea down – but usually I sketch it out and have to do it properly the very next day, whenever that's possible.

'Overall, it's a valuable addition to my life. In particular the many contacts I've made are often very helpful. I've made a few friends as well as new team members have joined.'

Angela
'The most time-consuming work is digging up the most up-to-date information and fitting it into the site. At the beginning I used to write a lot of the news, but now my life doesn't usually leave me much time for that.

'But the work you put in is rewarding. The site's been more successful than we could ever have dreamed when we planned it. It makes us really happy to see how our project is growing and that our readers enjoy our work.'

Is this your first website about a particular author and their work?

Isabella

'Yes, the first and the last. I couldn't run another site and still do it well. At the moment, I don't feel any need to.'

Angela

'I'd never done a website aimed at a larger audience either. This is the first really big, publicly visited website that I've been involved with and also the first which has concentrated on a particular author and their work. I have got ideas for other ones, but there just isn't enough time.'

How have your readers responded?

Isabella

'Mainly positively. We've already had e-mails from fans thanking us. Almost every day we get appreciative e-mails and entries in the visitors' book. We haven't had any really negative opinions, although that could be because the people who don't like our site don't bother telling us. But we can live with that just fine.'

Do you know approximately how many of the visitors to your site are male and female and how old they are on average?

Isabella

'I think it's mainly girls. I haven't met many Twilight-guys, as male readers like to call themselves. One hundred per cent of e-mails come from females. We are, of course, very happy to see any male visitors! We did have one male in our forum for a while. As far as age goes it's very mixed. We've had e-mails from readers over thirty as well as many from teenagers, generally from about thirteen years old. Our youngest forum member is twelve.'

How important do you think the internet has been in Stephenie Meyer's success?

Isabella
'I wasn't there right from the beginning, but I do think the internet was a particular help in getting the books out there. In the early days anyone could contact Stephenie directly via her website, which meant you could also make contact with other interesting people. For example, that's how I keep in contact with the founder of the official English fan page, the *Twilight Lexicon*, which was of course another big step up the ladder for Stephenie's career.'

Angela
'I think the internet was a really big factor in her success. Without the net I probably wouldn't have stumbled across her books, because Isabella and I met through a forum for discussing books. I'd seen the books often enough in bookshops, but never had any interest in them until I noticed that people in the forum were really excited about them. It's also fun knowing that you can be kept informed by the author, or even make contact directly, e.g. via a MySpace page.'

How important do you think the '*Twilight* boom' has been in encouraging reading? And for writing? Do you encourage fanfiction and keep up with the continuing internet development of the *Twilight* books?

Isabella
'The *Twilight* books have got a lot of young people reading more. I think when a person who doesn't like reading finds the right book, then that can get them on to reading other books, which maybe give the same feeling of satisfaction. For example, I have a friend who never used to read, I lent her a thriller one day and she'd devoured it inside of two days. Since then she's been a regular reader and likes to borrow books from me. It just has to click with the person reading and it would seem Stephenie Meyer's books click with a lot of people.

'Personally, I really like reading fan-fiction. One of my favourite writers has just published her own book. She got into writing through *Twilight* and trying to write fan-fiction. I think that's fantastic!'

Angela
'I think the *Twilight* books have a similar effect to the *Harry Potter* books. When they came out, the same thing happened; many young people said it was the first book they'd read with real pleasure. Whether this lasts, however, is very varied. For some it certainly remains a one-off trip into the world of reading – I know a few cases where once the series was read, that was

the end of it. Others, however, discover how wonderful books are and will continue to read. That's what I think is great about the *Twilight* boom because from childhood I've always loved reading and read a lot. I think people who don't read miss out on a lot. A few of our own forum members say that before reading the *Twilight* books they either didn't read at all, or not much. So I think that any books which excite young people this much help encourage reading.

'When you look at how much fan-fiction there is, I really think a lot of young people, and maybe adults, have got into writing as well through reading the *Twilight* books. Just think about Stephenie's own story: she had a dream, wrote a book on the back of it and has achieved worldwide success. It's a Cinderella story and maybe gives people the courage to elaborate on their own ideas. Tuomari, one of our team members, is writing her own book at the moment, which some of us are reading and we can usually hardly wait for her to give us each new chapter.

'We're really happy when forum members publish their work on our site. Although we do have to ask that it remains suitable for younger readers. Sadly we have had to delete a few things which were simply too risqué, as our youngest readers are only twelve.

'Personally, I don't read much fan-fiction; apart from one American lady's story, I find most of the attempts rather unconvincing, because basically I'm the kind of person who'd rather read what the author her – or himself sees in their world.'

Do you think there are some delicate issues? Like too much eroticism or too much Mormonism?

Isabella

'The books are children's books, but there are still many intimate moments, although the sexual act is never actually described in detail nor does it become tasteless. Of course I sometimes think, "Wow, I never read anything like that when I was thirteen", but actually we're surrounded by eroticism all the time. Today's young people seem to deal differently with it than when I was young (which isn't even all that long ago). But of course we have to keep our site and the forum as clean as possible, sometimes toning things down a bit, like some threads where people sometimes post photos of stars (like Robert Pattinson as Edward Cullen) which aren't entirely innocent! And of course we have to keep an eye on the fan-fiction page.

'When I write for the site I often ask myself, 'Would I want my (as yet non-existent) child reading something like this?' That usually helps to neatly avoid certain topics, or to rephrase them more innocently. Once I was a bit nervous as to whether particular photos of a female *Twilight* star weren't just a little too risqué. So I put in a link, rather than posting them directly on the page.'

Angela

'I really don't think the theme of intimacy in the *Twilight* books is a problem. In my opinion, the more intimate scenes aren't problematic because they're dealt with tastefully. Young people nowadays are probably used to a lot more since we're faced with eroticism all over the place.

'Although I must say, I didn't find *Breaking Dawn* quite so suitable for younger readers. There were moments where I thought I wouldn't want my thirteen or fourteen year-old daughter reading this. And I found Mormonism really noticeable for the first time.'

Is it a problem that Stephenie Meyer is a Mormon? Do you think her religion is a big influence in her books?

Isabella
'The fact that Stephenie's a Mormon isn't noticeable at all, in my opinion. Of course, there's no sex before marriage and there are discussions about souls, heaven and hell but that doesn't necessarily make you think of Mormonism straightaway. Intimacy (which is only natural) isn't swept under the carpet, but is dealt with quite openly without becoming tasteless or jeopardising the welfare of younger readers. Just the fact that she's writing about vampires shows she's not necessarily letting religion influence her books.'

Angela
'Stephenie's religious beliefs don't noticeably influence the first three books. After all, believing in no sex before marriage isn't exclusive to Mormonism. In the fourth book, however, I think the Mormon philosophy is clearly a big influence.'

Do you think it's a good thing that the *Twilight* films have been so successful? Or do you think there's a danger that the books will be marginalised?

Isabella
'I think it's more likely that the films will make people more interested in the books.

'Although I have to say, I wasn't all that happy about films being made at first. The *Twilight* books were like a secret and it was more personal to be in on the secret. The films mean more fans and that means sharing the books, so to speak. I suppose it's a bit like having to let your child grow up. It's difficult, but once you've done it, you're just proud that your child can stand on its own two feet. That's how I feel about the films. Of course the books can never be topped, however good Robert Pattinson is as Edward. My "head Edward", the Edward I saw while I was reading, he's the one who'll stick around.'

Angela
'Generally I'm not that keen on films of books. I find most of those kind of films disappointing, maybe because I've got quite high expectations. There are only two films of books that I found almost as good as the books themselves – both of them were serials (*Lord of the Rings*, and the BBC's *Pride and Prejudice*).

'Apart from my own subjective view on films of books, I also think that in terms of encouraging young people to read, they're counter-productive. Some young people will think, "Why read, when I can just watch the film?" I think you miss a lot if you don't experience the story yourself in your own head cinema. In my opinion, films can add to a book at best, but never replace it.'

How do you see yourselves continuing this website?

Isabella
'I've given that quite a lot of thought, obviously. I think as long as the films are around and there's still news on the subject, we'll still be here. Unless we get squeezed out by other sites and it's not worth it any more. But I think if we keep on working as hard as we do, then (hopefully) that's not going to happen. If there's a new film every year, then I reckon we've got a good two or three years left. After that we'll just have to see what happens. I'm sure Stephenie's not going to stop writing and *Midnight Sun* (*Twilight* from Edward's point of view) might even get published in the future. *Twilight*'s going to be making news for a few years yet, I'm sure of it.'

Angela
'I'm just going to see what happens. When the news begins to dry up and there aren't any more new books or films coming out, then it'll be time to think about what to do when the *Twilight* boom slows down and visitor numbers drop off. Then we'll have to ask ourselves how much sense it makes to keep working on the site. The site will, however, definitely continue to exist long-term as a source of information, even once there's nothing new to report.'

Isabella and *Angela*

'We'd like to say a huge thank you to all our fantastic readers and team members! Without you, we could never have been the big, up-to-date fan-site we're so pleased we are.'

A lot of fans feel that the series has impacted on many aspects of their daily lives, from internet chatting topics to forming friendships over it!

'As a fifteen-year-old Twilighter, I link a lot of things from my everyday life with the saga, like for example, manners, character traits or experiences. Like when I'm too excited or nervous, I say something like, "Where's Jasper when you need him?" Every day I talk about all sorts of things from the saga with my two best Twilighter friends.'

'I think a lot about the relationship between Bella and Edward and whether it's too intense . . . Whether the two of them are too dependent on each other.'

'I often think I was born in the wrong century. A hundred years earlier and I'm pretty sure I'd have found someone at least similar to Edward, because it's his manners and his pure thoughts towards Bella that make him most attractive to me. Men like that are sadly few and far between nowadays, because most men of my age are looking for adventure rather than for the right woman.'

'When you find your true love, someone you want to spend the rest of your life with, then I think you've found your very own Edward.'

'When I see teenagers in the bus, in the supermarket or around town, I really can't see any link between them and the pretty middle-class teenagers in *Twilight*. Harmless dates, prom nights and holding hands are not exactly comparable with drunk fourteen year-olds and parties, which can be more like orgies than parties. *Twilight* presents an almost romantic view of the world, where each of the female protagonists wants to fall in love, and does. But each love story comes across as being serious, passionate and grown up. All of which is a long way from my experience of people. Of course there are always exceptions, but I really haven't met many young people who come across as that responsible. Perhaps these disappear in the shadow of the "bored-of-everything-think-I'll-get-drunk" teens. That's the very reason I find it almost comforting that in addition to the adults there are so many teenagers interested in *Twilight*.'

'In school we're always quoting from the book, like, "What if I'm not a superhero? What if I'm the bad guy?", that's our absolute top favourite quote. When one person starts the quote, someone else finishes it. That really annoys the boys on our table, because it's the only thing we talk about.'

'At the end of last year, I was completely in love with the

Twilight books and was just reading the second book. Since I couldn't put the book down or stop reading, I obviously took it to school with me. After my English class I took the book straight out of my bag so I could read it during break. Before I got through the door, my teacher called me over. She asked if it was *Twilight* I was holding. Of course I said yes. My teacher was enthusiastic and told me she'd just finished the third book and that she loved the series more than anything else. She also asked me if I'd fallen a little bit in love with Edward, like she had (by the way, this teacher was still young, just twenty-six). She told me she really got on her husband's nerves, because she was always telling him how marvellous Edward was. After we'd talked about the book for a while, she asked me if I was looking forward to reading the third book, since I was nearly finished with the second. Of course I could hardly wait, but I told her I had to wait about another week before I could buy the third book. She was shocked and said it was real torture when you've finished one book and can't keep on reading.

'The next day I arrived at school early and was waiting for the first bell when I saw my teacher running towards me. She stopped halfway and told me to wait a moment. She ran into the staffroom and came back with a blue cotton bag which she handed me with a broad grin and told me to look inside. I was completely amazed. My teacher had brought me *Eclipse* so that I could read it over the long weekend instead of having to wait a week. It was so nice of her I couldn't thank her enough. At the end of the year we had to make a poster about a book of our choice. Of course I chose *Twilight* and the poster is still up in our classroom, even though we have a new teacher. Since my old teacher's classroom is opposite, I still go over sometimes and have a short chat with her about the most recent *Twilight* news.'

✦

TWILIGHT
AND
LITERATURE

It's intriguing to look at the narrative devices employed by Stephenie Meyer in her *Twilight* saga and also to examine the literary references and influences which enrich the four novels.

'I' is the first word of the preface to the first book – 'I' being Bella Swan, the first person narrator of the story. At the beginning of *Twilight* she's seventeen years old. She seems older. Thinking about how sensible Bella is, her mother Renée likes to joke that she was already thirty-five years old when she was born.

One of the most interesting narrative elements of the *Twilight* series is clear to see in the chapter *Interrogations* in *Twilight*. In this chapter, Bella tries to explain to Edward how completely average she is. She says she just isn't anything special – particularly in the face of his perfection. When he hears this, he criticises her, saying she 'doesn't see herself very clearly'. He refers to what 'every human male was thinking' on her first day at Forks High School. He says she's quite the 'opposite of ordinary'.

What does this scene mean for the reader of the *Twilight* saga? If the first person narrator doesn't see herself clearly, then perhaps she doesn't see other characters clearly either. And a number of things do suggest – as Edward claims – that Bella's self-image is a little distorted. The reader has seen just how quickly numerous male admirers rush up to help her. There is a lot of evidence to suggest that Edward is right, that Bella is indeed a very attractive young lady.

The first person narrator, however, is the only source, the only guide through the *Twilight* saga. The reader is completely and utterly dependent on her. So, Bella doesn't see herself as attractive but as just ordinary. Which version is right? Bella's modest view of herself, or Edward's enthusiasm about her charms?

It's a difficult decision for the reader. Bella is a wonderful observer, a precise chronicler of events, but clearly she sometimes misjudges other characters and herself. This uncertainty, this imperfect source, is a fascinating narrative element which accompanies the reader through the entire *Twilight* saga. For who can claim without a shadow of a doubt to be able to judge themselves and their effect on others with absolute precision? No one. So Bella's weakness becomes a further endearing characteristic that the reader is glad to identify with. At the same time this weakness allows Stephenie to play around with ideas of appearance and reality, with fact and fiction.

Why does the reader identify so quickly with Bella? It helps that she is a first person narrator, but she is a very particular one. Bella's memories come across as very authentic. That has to do with the fact that Bella names the weaknesses of others, which show up her own strengths. It also has to do with the fact that she is upfront about her own weaknesses – for example, that she blushes all the time.

How does Stephenie tell the story? What techniques does she employ to hold her readers' attention? She works hard at this, right from the preface of the first book, where Bella begins her tale with some thoughts on life and death in the midst of a truly dramatic moment, just as a hunter threatens her life. Bella's convinced she's about to be killed. In one short page we are introduced to events that won't be picked up again until much further on in the story. This creates an arc of suspense. And the reader can hope that Bella, the first person narrator, did survive this dramatic moment, however hopeless the situation might seem – how else could Bella be telling the story of this moment and the events that led up to it?

New Moon also begins with a preface in which Bella is facing grave danger. The structure is identical to book one and is repeated again in *Eclipse*, where Bella wonders whether she'll live long enough to find out the outcome of a battle which is taking place simultaneously. So, will Bella live to tell the story of her rebirth as a vampire? The reader feels sure she will! However, the repeated change of narrator in books three and four might give rise to some doubt. When the story is suddenly told exclusively from Jacob's point of view, it allows for the possibility that Bella might really die. But Stephenie varies the pattern in book four. There are similarities in how close death is, and the danger-ridden situations, but action is no longer in the foreground; no more wild chases or bloody violence, instead love is the most important thing.

The preface to the second book in *Breaking Dawn* is unusually short, but here too, in just one sentence, the topic is a life and death situation. The preface to the third book of *Breaking Dawn* is where it returns to the established pattern: Bella's in an inescapable situation and about to be murdered. It's impressive that the author, in this case, proceeds differently; Stephenie resists fulfilling the expectation her pattern suggests, pleasing her more curious readers.

BORN OF LITERATURE

Literature is born of literature. Stephenie makes no secret of this – quite the contrary, she cleverly integrates literature into her *Twilight* saga.

No other school subject is mentioned so often in the series as English. For example, Bella mentions Act III of *Macbeth*, about which she has to write an essay. The topic Bella has chosen is whether Shakespeare's depiction of female characters is misogynistic. When she's not reading for school, she reads her well-thumbed Jane Austen books that she brought with her to Forks. Her favourite books are *Pride and Prejudice* and *Sense and Sensibility*. She's re-reading the latter when Edward is trying to keep her at a distance and notices that the hero is called Edward. So she changes to *Mansfield Park* – only to realise the hero there is Edmund, which is still too close for comfort. Were there no other names in late-eighteenth century novels, she asks herself in annoyance. Just as *Twilight* fans re-read their favourite books, so Bella reads and re-reads *Wuthering Heights*. Bella's reading sets landmarks, structures the story. For example, at the beginning of *Eclipse* when Charlie awkwardly tries to get her out and about, she has gotten as far as Heathcliff's return.

It's beyond doubt that Stephenie has invested her heroine Bella with her own love of literature. Her sensitivity to handwriting is part of that love. *Eclipse* begins with a letter from Jacob for which the publisher has chosen a special font, with added ink splatters and crossed through words. This is designed to show the pain Jacob was in as he wrote. Bella also feels this as she reads his message, but Jacob's suffering hurts her more even than her own. So as she looks at Jacob's hurtful lines, it seems to her that each stroke of each crossed out letter is like a small dagger.

Despite, or perhaps as a result of, her love of language and her broad reading, Bella sometimes finds it difficult to find the right words, or she avoids them because they're too strange to her. At the beginning of *Eclipse*, Bella is trying to find a good word to describe Edward. 'Boyfriend' doesn't seem right, because it doesn't have the ring of eternal commitment. On the other hand, she thinks terms like fate and destiny seem self-important. Stephenie shows how Bella's sensitivity to language affects her storytelling and it's moments like this that make the *Twilight* saga so worth reading.

The literary background to the *Twilight* saga is an integral part of its success. Literature plays an important role in the series. Right at the beginning, Bella makes light of the reading list that Mr Mason, her English teacher, has given her: Brontë, Shakespeare, Chaucer and Faulkner, all of which, she says, are 'fairly basic', which is comforting, but also makes her think there's a danger she may be bored in class. Not so readers of Stephenie's *Twilight* saga. Not many readers of Bella and Edward's adventures will be able to say of those authors that they've 'already read everything'.

One special characteristic of the *Twilight* saga is that it constantly creates links between itself and other great works of literature and so can function as a (re-)entry point into literary works that may have been spoiled by a school experience. At the beginning of *Eclipse*, Bella and Edward are talking about *Wuthering Heights*. Edward complains that Cathy and Heathcliff are compared with couples like Romeo and Juliet or Elizabeth Bennet and Mr Darcy. He says *Wuthering Heights* isn't a love story but a 'hate story'. Bella replies that she's fascinated by the inevitability in *Wuthering Heights* – neither Cathy's selfishness, nor Heathcliff's evil, nor even death can separate them. The only good quality in these two protagonists, she says, is their love, and in a longer conversation, Bella and Edward later compare their life with Cathy and Heathcliff's.

Wuthering Heights is a book within a book and the *Twilight* saga is the best advert for it. It's fantastic that Stephenie's fans are being led right back to the roots of the *Twilight* saga, which in turn can lead to a whole new set of reading material. This is why I am convinced that Stephenie's books are far more important in the fight to encourage young people to read than any preceding young adult bestsellers have been. In comparison, for example, to *Harry Potter* which can lead fans to read other, usually worse, fantasy titles, Stephenie leads readers 'upward'. She encourages fans to give the classics a go, and she's persistent about it. A few hundred pages after the conversation mentioned above, Edward comes back to this topic. The more time he spends with Bella, the more human emotions make sense to him and when he re-reads *Wuthering Heights*, he realises he now sympathises with Heathcliff more than he would have thought possible. After their midnight chat about literature, Bella finds her dog-eared copy of *Wuthering Heights* lying open on the floor where Edward dropped it and Bella reads the words that Heathcliff spoke which so impressed Edward: 'The moment her regard ceased, I would have torn his heart out, and drank his blood! But, till then – if you don't believe me, you don't know me – I would have died by inches before I touched a single hair of his head!'

THE TRUTH OF OLD STORIES

Each of Stephenie's four books was inspired by a quite specific literary model: *Twilight* is *Pride and Prejudice*. In *New Moon* there is a strong link with *Romeo and Juliet*. *Eclipse* is Stephenie's homage to *Wuthering Heights*. In *Breaking Dawn*, two tales play an important role: *A Midsummer Night's Dream* and *The Merchant of Venice*, with which, amongst other things, she explains the absence of a battle, the showdown which doesn't happen – or rather which happens only in their thoughts – in short, it's her reason for the absence of violence at the end of the *Twilight* saga. The peaceful ending, the all-encompassing happy end annoyed a number of readers, who had become used to a lot of fighting at the end of each book. For the grand finale, Stephenie didn't feel that a story has only been told well if it takes the worst possible turn of events. No tragedy, no death at the end of the *Twilight* saga: in this Stephenie created the biggest possible surprise for the reader.

But Stephenie Meyer is no stranger to creating tension when she wants to. Bella develops an almost schizophrenic behaviour that stretches the reader on a rack of suspense as she tries to find the truth about the Cullens, creating a willingness to accept the inevitable conclusion. This state of unknowing persists for a long time, so long that the reader is led gently – more gently than in most fantasy novels – and in the end willingly and trustingly into the supernatural world of vampires and werewolves. Over the course of hundreds of pages there's a departure from logic and common sense and, at the same time, a slow discovery of the supernatural. This too makes Stephenie's *Twilight* saga stand apart from other stories.

Two-thirds of the way into *Twilight*, after Bella's first visit to the Cullens' house, the tension threatens to abate. Bella and Edward have confessed their love to each other, they're affectionate with each other and it's public knowledge. The love story seems to be told. The peculiarities of a relationship between a human and a vampire have been explained. What next?

The new action element is introduced by Edward. He tells Bella that he will seem over-protective for the next few weeks because Alice has foreseen visitors.

Once the tracker, James, has turned up, the story changes genre for the last hundred pages of the book. Edward displays nerves and Bella shows impressive good sense. The emergency situation is such that Bella is forced to hurt Charlie in order to get away from him as quickly as possible.

Edward and Bella are apart for the first time because of James. Their eyes burn into each other before they part. The danger that James poses can't be underestimated. With the help of his intuition and experience, he almost succeeds in deceiving the Cullens and murdering Bella. The love story has become less important – the plot becomes that of a thriller, a showdown for the book with a truly impressive crescendo. For the first time the consequences of this misalliance become absolutely apparent: by being together, Edward and Bella are putting a lot of other people in danger too. Initially it's mainly Charlie and Renée, but later the Cullens and the werewolves too.

FLESH AND BLOOD

A first person narrator with the ability to be self-critical is one of Stephenie's most important lessons for all readers who may be thinking about writing. Luckily, Stephenie increases her protagonist's expressive power by having Bella reveal all her facets, which show off her talents and abilities: Bella describes herself as having a strong voice. Bella deems it an advantage that she's able to suppress unpleasant things. Just before her near-death scene in book one she reveals the extent of her willpower. After writing a farewell letter to Edward, she seals first the letter, and then, carefully, her heart. Right at the beginning, she was afraid she would lose her sense of humour and sarcasm in Forks. With reference to her pale skin, she said to Eric that her mother was half albino, which the boy takes seriously. During the course of the *Twilight* saga, Bella proves repeatedly that she has retained her sense of humour. When she has to make a decision, she agonises over it, but once made she follows through on it. She ought to be afraid of Edward, but generally she doesn't feel able to be afraid of him. Bella is in fact extraordinarily brave.

Bella can also be quite forward. The first time she speaks with Billy Black about the problems between the Cullens and the people living on the Reservation, nobody actually comes out and calls a spade a spade, but the conversation is clearly pregnant with the knowledge the reader has gleaned about vampires and werewolves. It's even more interesting that Bella can come across as really quite arrogant, in particular in relation to other boys like Mike, who she imagines as a faithful dog wagging his tail. Of course she doesn't let him see that, but the reader wonders at a character sometimes so riddled with self-doubt and at other times so pompous.

She's also confident in relation to her mother, Renée, and her father, Charlie. For one she provides food, for the other she provides emotional mothering. She speaks of Renée in exactly the same way a mother would of her child. Renée had to lead her own life sometime. Bella admits to having had an indulgent, amused and slightly condescending attitude to her mother. Bella saw numerous weaknesses in her and, privately, laughed to herself about them.

Bella herself has always thought she's somehow different – a freak. Jacob puts it well when he says normal people run away from monsters. Edward seems to confirm that she is abnormal by the fact he can't hear her thoughts. In this point the reader is one step ahead of Edward for a change. The reader hears Bella's voice, reads her thoughts and admires their authenticity.

More Intense Feelings

Is there anything Stephenie could have done better here? There are only a very few points which niggle: Bella describes herself and her father as being not exactly 'verbose'. Neither of them is much good at putting their feelings into words. That stands in rather stark contrast to the nearly 3,000 pages of the *Twilight* saga, where Bella tells her exciting and highly emotional story.

Many creative writing courses teach that a first person narrator should look in the mirror, by chapter three at the latest, so that the author has an opportunity to describe the character's appearance. It's a little bit of a cliché but Stephenie Meyer employs it in book one. Right at the beginning of chapter one, Bella looks at herself in the mirror for a long time, describing what she sees, in particular her skin, her pale mirror image, which she thinks will look even more pasty and unhealthy in shady Forks than it did in sunny Phoenix, where it at least had a little colour.

This scene and other narrative techniques would suggest that Stephenie Meyer was listening a little more carefully in her creative writing class than she admitted to in our interview. But then, many students do creative writing courses and never go on to write an international bestseller. There's much more to capturing the reader's attention the way Stephenie does than simply following a few creative writing rules and it's interesting to note that Stephenie also often breaks with convention. The further into the *Twilight* saga she gets, the more often she builds in flashbacks. For example, a conversation from the past is reconsidered, but a few pages later she's back in the present. It's a narrative technique most writing schools warn against using; it can restrict the pace of the story too much and demand too much of the reader's imagination and memory. Nor are radical changes of perspective recommended by teachers of creative writing. A few pages at the end of *Eclipse* is written from

Jacob's point of view, and the perspective shifts even more in *Breaking Dawn*.

Conflicts are dealt with in ways that go far beyond anything taught in writing schools. Right up to the moment Bella and Edward become engaged there are an amazing number of arguments between the two young lovers, but clearly without ever endangering their underlying love. The trigger is sometimes Bella's longing for Jacob, sometimes Edward's secretiveness when danger's looming. When she goes from Jacob to Edward and vice versa, their two super-noses always prompt them to tell her how much she stinks of dog or vampire. When Edward is taken to task, his eyes go hard and cold like the night or glitter angrily. Which is a good thing, because if they only ever glowed like warm amber the reader would soon grow bored. Arguments give zest to the plot and so are crucial to the narrative. This is another aspect of the *Twilight* saga that makes it special: the everyday conflicts of relationships, the natural feelings of jealousy and the need for personal space are intensified by the supernatural elements.

The conversation Edward and Bella have about age, when Edward reveals the incredible fact that he was born in 1901 in Chicago, could take place between any two people where the man is significantly older than the woman. Despite the bizarre content, this discussion feels very authentic because it's so realistic. Real life is often mirrored in the series – the story is easier to identify with than is often the case when reading fantasy, as Stephenie puts so much of our known world and reality into her text. Essentially *Twilight* is a passionate love story between teenagers, but it is enriched by the fantastical element of vampires, which each reader can choose to make more or less of – in fact, it's possible to play down the fantasy elements to such an extent that they can be read as a very close comment on to daily life. The story can then be re-examined or looked at from a quite new perspective. What girl hasn't had the problem of a boy who fancies her, although she isn't at all interested in him, if for no other reason than that he's too young? And at the same time that girl fancies a boy who seems utterly perfect and unattainable. And, hey presto, she can see her own real life reflected in the pages of the *Twilight* saga.

A Lighter Side

What would the *Twilight* saga be without humour? The *Twilight* books provoke excitement and tears, but more often than that they make the reader smile or laugh. For example, there's comedy in Bella's sudden changes of tone: the attempted blood typing is a scene of this nature. A crescendo of suffering describes Bella's discomfort, moving from a cold sweat breaking out on her forehead and a churning stomach to a growing rushing in her ears and dizzy spells. Her friends don't yet know that she faints at the sight of blood. But when Edward sees her in this state she says she wants '. . . to die. Or, at the very least, not to throw up'. This abrupt change of tone which happens frequently in the *Twilight* saga is sure to make the reader laugh out loud.

The conversations between Bella and Edward also sparkle with comedy. When Edward first tells Bella the Cullens like to feed on bears, Bella underplays her shock and fright with quick humour: she retorts that it's not the hunting season. Clearly it works to keep the situation light, because Edward takes up the joke and points out that the law only forbids hunting with weapons. The jokey exchange could end there, but the underlying dimension of fear allows them to on go into a conversation about the feeding habits of the Cullen family. We learn that Edward prefers pumas, that the Cullens are careful to concentrate on areas with too many predators and that they always take the environment into consideration. The reader is entertained and informed in this manner throughout the series, but the variations can be a bit cheeky: besides the factual information about feeding habits, besides the comedy it creates alongside fear, this passage also subtly suggests associations with other, similar confessions of a more intimate nature. The inexperienced female asks the male questions about a taboo topic ('What do you like [best to feed on]?') and hears secrets which at first make her shudder, but which she will soon grow comfortable with. And even while still talking, the male tries to reduce the female's anxiety exaggerating some details ('Nothing more fun than an irritated grizzly bear') in order to relax the situation with laughter.

The level of understanding, which amuses the reader in

relation to vampires, is sometimes itself part of the story. For example, Edward remembers Bella's human hunger, suggesting it is 'breakfast time', which makes Bella clutch her throat with both hands, looking at him anxiously. Edward is shocked and Bella giggles, 'Kidding'. He still doesn't find it funny. So he clarifies, 'Breakfast time for the human'.

Edward's ability to read everybody's thoughts except Bella's also provides a broad canvas for humour. He 'listens' to the people Bella talks to and draws conclusions about how she must be feeling. This type of scene never goes on for long enough.

FULL OF SURPRISES

Stephenie also masters the game of cliché and exaggeration with brilliance. According to Edward, Esme is so happy about Bella that she wouldn't mind if Bella had a third eye or webbed feet. When Charlie tries to make spaghetti, Bella has to use a steak knife to cut the lumps of pasta into two portions. When Bella's at home alone, after she's started talking to the magnets on the fridge door, she accuses them of being stubborn because they won't sit comfortably next to each other, and she leaves the house in a rush before the magnets supposedly have a chance to start answering her. Memorably, Edward teases Bella the first time she comes to his house, after she mentions she's surprised there are no coffins, and lets her know that 'I don't even think we have cobwebs'.

It's also comic when Edward and Bella play at the worst-case scenario and the reader knows they're only having fun with the vampire situation. This adds another layer to the story. We see them playing the first time Bella goes to the Cullens' house, when Edward jokingly leaps at Bella and, with mischief in his eyes, scares her until she admits that he's a 'very, very terrifying monster'. And Alice joins in too, saying, 'It sounded like you were having Bella for lunch, and we came to see if you would share'. At another point, when Bella and Edward are thinking about where to live once she's been changed, Bella suggests Antarctica. She couldn't kill anybody there, she says, and Edward sniffs contemptuously, 'Penguins. Delicious'. And so there is humour to be found even in the seemingly serious scenes.

Whether the humour is always deliberate is another question. Supposedly serious scenes, such as when Bella is leaning up against Jacob in wolf form, can sometimes strain the reader's imagination. But who knows, perhaps the author wrote this with a smile? 'It's all fun' was something Stephenie never grew tired of saying during our interview on the train between Munich and Cologne.

When Bella tells Charlie that she and Edward are together, Charlie says he's really too old for her. Bella retorts that they're in the same school year, but she thinks: if he only knew how right he is. How little Bella's parents know about the real situation is also a source of humour, such as at the end of *Twilight* : 'My mom was here and I was recovering from a vampire attack.' There are so many reasons to read the *Twilight* saga with great pleasure! With tears too, of course. It's really impressive that at the beginning of *New Moon* – when the Cullens have left and Bella has sunk into a deep depression and the reader is suffering with her – the publishers were willing to print nine pages containing a total of only four words. That's even more generous than in a book of poetry. Empty pages symbolising an empty life. Just the names of the months in which nothing happens.

Stephenie also works consciously with paradox. When Bella first sees the five Cullens sitting in the cafeteria, away from all the other students, she begins her detailed description of them with the sentence, 'They didn't look anything alike', then a little later she clarifies, 'and yet, they were all exactly alike'.

First she draws out all the differences and then she emphasises similarities. In this way she maintains the reader's attention, if that were necessary. The reader's attention is guaranteed while reading the *Twilight* saga.

CROSS-OVER

Stephenie Meyer's *Twilight* books are unusual and carefully crafted in another way too: they appeal strongly to different generations; both teenagers and their mothers are gripped by its excitement.

Claudia Cremer, a high school teacher, heard about the *Twilight* series from her students. Her responses to my questions are very revealing.

When and how did you discover your first Stephenie Meyer book?

'I would get the students to introduce a novel of their choice in the ten minutes at the beginning of double lessons. Last year one student chose to present *Twilight* by Stephenie Meyer. She was really excited about it and recommended all the girls in the class to read it. I wasn't all that interested, as up until then I didn't really like vampire stories at all. But my student was very insistent – even giving me her copy to read. Which I did and was promptly hooked! As soon as I'd finished that one, I borrowed the next two and waited impatiently for the fourth to come out.'

What do you like best about Stephenie Meyer's *Twilight* saga?

'Well, the love story between Bella and Edward, of course! The main characters: Bella – clumsy, stubborn, with her slightly rebellious and unconventional ways; Edward, the dream guy; Charlie, whose bark is worse than his bite, with his heart in the right place; the vampire family – all the various family members and their history. Then Jacob, from *New Moon* onward! The American college atmosphere, daily life for teenagers in a small town. Dreary old Forks. The underlying threat from the Volturi, which ensures ongoing suspense. Edward's thoughts on immortality and being a vampire.'

Do you have other favourite books, which you like even better?

'Jane Austen's novels – in particular *Pride and Prejudice*.

'Kate Atkinson – all of her novels, without exception.

'Margaret Atwood – *The Blind Assassin*.

'Margaret Laurence – all the novels from the *Manawaka* cycle.

'Women's literature in general, without any vampires or any supernatural elements, although my newest favourite novel is Stephenie Meyer's *The Host*!'

Do you see differences between Stephenie Meyer's *Twilight* saga and other fantasy novels?

'I rarely read fantasy novels, so I can't really comment. J.R.R. Tolkien's *Lord of the Rings* and Marion Zimmer Bradley's *Mists of Avalon* are a similar kind of thing. But I think that in Stephenie Meyer's books the love story element is far more in the foreground than is usual for fantasy.'

Does your mother or do other adult women you know read the *Twilight* series?

'I thought about lending Stephenie Meyer's *Twilight* saga to my eighty-year-old aunt or maybe to my seventy-four-year-old mother-in-law. They both devour all kinds of books, including love stories. I decided not to in the end, though, because I think they would be put off by the implied and then later actual sex scenes (with a vampire, between vampires). I felt it was too "modern" for them.

'But I did recommend the series to a variety of colleagues aged between thirty and fifty who enjoy romance literature and – without exception – they all loved it. I think you have to have loved and read romantic stories as a girl to be able to get this kind of enjoyment as an adult. It's really important to have memories of reading from when you were young.'

What do you talk about most with other readers, when you're discussing the *Twilight* series?

'Mostly about the romantic relationship – is Edward really the ultimate dream man, or is he just a bit too good? Should Bella really be with Edward, or Jacob?

'Is immortality really worth wanting? Does Bella make the right decision in becoming a vampire?

'Why do we women like love stories so much?

'Can you tell from her books that Stephenie Meyer is a Mormon?

'Is Stephenie Meyer not a little warped?'

Would you like to live in a family like the Cullens' and be immortal?

'No, how awful!'

Do you identify with Bella?

'Yes, definitely. She's not perfect, she's a typical teenager, rebellious, independent, searching for the love of her life, making mistakes, but no really bad ones. She loves sincerely, is constant, loyal, daring, sometimes cheeky, humorous, self-critical, self-mocking, likes reading . . .'

Do you think a boy like Edward could ever exist in real life?

'No! It would be awful, anyway! But there are, of course, plenty of men who share some of his good qualities. My husband, for example!'

As you're reading, do you sometimes see Edward's vampire desires in terms of a 'normal boy's' erotic wishes?

'Of course! I think that's the intention. Edward loves Bella's scent. Smell is the most intense and most sensual way of experiencing another human being. How could the attractiveness of a woman be more strongly described than through her scent (see Patrick Süsskind, *Perfume*). Then there's the pulsing blood, the colour red, the drinking of blood (taste being the second most intense sense) – all signalling passion and sensuousness. How could anyone not think of sex?'

Do you believe vampires exist?

'No.'

What (happy) ending would you like for Bella and Edward?

'I wish Bella hadn't become a vampire. In the film *Highlander*, the main character is immortal but his wife still ages naturally and dies in the end. He loves her to the end and buries her. I thought that was very emotional. I probably prefer the *Highlander* ending because I'm already over forty, so any dream of eternal youth is long gone.'

What do you think the *Twilight* series and its massive international success says about today's young people? Do you agree with the comment 'At least young people are still reading'?

'"At least young people are still reading", I can certainly testify to that as far as girls are concerned. I think it's great that girls are still enjoying a good romance and dreaming of finding the love of their life. But I'm not sure they read the books quite the way I do.'

Do you think Bella is an anti-feminist heroine and that she sacrifices too much for her love of Edward?

'Basically Bella is a very modern young woman. She is egotistical, follows her own objectives single-mindedly and persistently. She is willing to let others suffer (her father, Jacob, even Edward) so that she can be with Edward forever. Her own interests are paramount.

'Really it's Edward who sacrifices everything for Bella, even his dignity. His offer to let Jacob get Bella pregnant, so that she can have the child she longs for (a replacement for Edward's baby which endangers her life) is almost unbearable.'

It would seem that even adult readers experience the same sweep of emotions and puzzle over the same complexities of life presented by the *Twilight* saga as many of its younger readers. Perhaps this suggests that Stephenie Meyer's supposed children's books really tackle the greatest themes in love and life, creating a uniquely universal appeal. But what is it that everyone loves about the books? Here are some replies.

'There are three things I particularly like. First: Bella loves Edward, regardless of how dangerous it might be for her. The deep love described here is of a kind you hardly ever see nowadays. That's one of the things I love about the series. Second: I like the way Edward behaves. He always makes an effort to put Bella's wellbeing above his own. It's just great to read about how much he loves her and about all the things he does for her. Third: I admire the way the Cullen family sticks together. I grew up in a big family with lots of siblings and the way the Cullen family sticks together reminds me of that.'

'I can't say exactly, there's so much I love about the book. It's not just the story of Bella and Edward that I find so fascinating. I can't describe it very well, but reading these books just makes you feel good and uplifted.'

'I just like seeing that vampires aren't "so" wildly unrealistic. She's written it so that you can really get involved with the story. That even a "forbidden" love can survive if you fight for it.'

Again and again people are fascinated by how much they find realistic and true-to-life.

'I think it's great that you can identify with the story. I really had butterflies in my tummy during the first book, as if I'd just fallen in love myself and in the second I could really feel Bella's pain. No other books have done that for me.'

'You can really put yourself in Bella's shoes, you understand why she does what she does, because every tiny detail is written down. And that this love, which should be impossible, manages to survive.'

'I think it's particularly interesting that it's all written from the point of view of a young girl. The whole story gets a really personal feel because of that.'

Some people have a more general view and value the creativity and the literary qualities of the saga.

'I like that she's taken the age-old theme of vampires and completely reworked it.'

'I like the portrayal of the characters. It's enjoyable to read and very emotionally written. You can really feel the tension. Even though it's a bit strange at first, I like the change of narrators in books three and four. You get to know the other people better and you see Bella and the other characters from a new perspective.'

'The description of how love develops between Bella and Edward, the restrictions on intimacy because of the necessary distance, and later Bella's confusion at her attraction to Jacob.'

'I love that it's so realistic! She could have written about classic vampires who sleep in coffins and wear long black cloaks. But then the story wouldn't be so good. The love story really fits well into the book! Altogether I love that the book fits into so many genres . . . drama, romance, horror.'

'I love that it isn't set in some "fantasy world". The creatures, that is the vampires and werewolves, live in our world amongst humans and yet almost nobody knows they exist.'

'The style of writing . . . it makes you feel seventeen again.'

'I like it so much because she's totally recreated vampire mythology.'

'I love that every detail is described in the book, which makes it feel very intimate and private. It's almost like a diary that's not intended for public consumption.'

'I love that you feel if you got in a plane and then in a taxi to Forks, that if you then walked about in the woods you might really bump into Edward, Bella or Jake.'

I asked the fans about the literary merits of the series, and if they thought that it was a good way to encourage reluctant readers.

'I don't know many people of my age (I'm fourteen) who read much. If I say I've been to the library or that I'm reading a good book, they tend to roll their eyes or call me things like "swot" or "bookworm". But I think those people would enjoy reading *Twilight*! But how will they ever know if they never even pick up a book? And I think the book is so successful because it's not the usual vampire story. Young people have problems during puberty, with love and the like, you know. And it's nice to read such a realistic "vampire-human romance", to get completely lost in it and then afterwards to dream about the gorgeous Edward Cullen . . .'

'Every new generation of young people has its own icons and role models. Stephenie Meyer's *Twilight* saga has surely given young people something new to be interested in.'

'Its success shows that young women and girls see their romantic ideal in this book; passionate/erotic feelings/fantasies are reflected in the book and the heroine's maturing and changing feelings are ones many young people will find it easy to identify with in their own lives. Basically, I think it's a really good thing if young people are reading and I can't find anything bad to say about *Twilight* as a starting point. Since reading it, by the way, my stepdaughter has been devouring tonnes of books on a variety of different subjects and even if some of it is real "trash", surely that's how you develop a sense for good literature, isn't it?'

'I could write a term paper on this topic! First of all I have to say how happy I am that today's young people are reading again. But I also think that young girls' attitudes and dreams are changing. Just look at Edward's character, he's certainly not the traditional boy of today.'

'The huge success of this saga shows that young people are not chronic non-readers. They're just very hard to please and *Twilight* has managed to comprise everything that moves young people. Just the right balance of love, action, thriller and humour, that's the *Twilight* saga! And as we clearly see, this combination works just as well for adult readers!'

'Firstly, the book is really easy to read (and I absolutely don't mean that as a criticism). No complicated, endlessly long sentences or tonnes of big words, so even non-bookworms can get into the book and feel involved in the story quickly. Also the plot reflects the chaos of feelings that pretty much everyone experiences sooner or later in life. I might be wrong, but I think that this book reminds young people that "old-fashioned values" are an option. Or is there a girl out there who's said: "I do love Edward, I only wish his manners weren't so nice." When you're reading a book your imagination is much less hampered and it's really important to be able to dream. It seems that's being rediscovered just now.'

It was also interesting to see how some people thought there was a clear line between the *Twilight* saga and fantasy.

'I think the biggest difference to fantasy literature is that what Stephenie Meyer describes could somehow be real. We don't know whether vampires exist or not, because they would make absolutely sure they stay hidden. Although I would like to add that I don't believe in vampires! But Stephenie Meyer's novels really draw so strongly on real life.'

'I think the reason for its appeal is the "reality" behind it. To everyone else, Edward's just a normal boy, they don't know his secret. The ones who don't know his secret, don't know about the existence of the paranormal either. He goes to school like everyone else, it's set in our time.'

'The *Twilight* series is almost reality, coupled with a myth that comes across so realistically it could actually exist.'

'In other fantasy novels you know you're not in a real world, but in this saga you keep thinking you are in a real world because it all starts so peacefully – like a usual love story.'

'Quite simply, it's the captivating love story, which is so deep and which you can understand one hundred per cent. And also that Meyer writes so unbelievably realistically and sensitively. Secretly, I still can't quite see it as fantasy. You get the feeling it could actually happen at any moment, that these unbelievably beautiful vampires might suddenly be sitting next to you in the canteen!'

'Meyer's saga can hardly be seen as typical fantasy, it's more a romantic novel. Fantasy elements in Meyer's work are kept to a minimum, a normal world, where the only unusual feature is the existence of vampires and werewolves. In particular the first two books have too little really thrilling action to be typical fantasy novels. They're purely about the Edward-Bella-Jacob relationship set against a background of various different lives. For a typical fantasy novel, there's simply too little action around the developing relationship between the two protagonists. In fantasy novels there's usually some kind of action at the centre of it against which the characters develop and build relationships. In Meyer's books it's purely about the development of the two characters and their relationship with each other, elements like the newborns' attack shift more into the background. In typical fantasy that would be different. I would place Meyer's saga more in a sub-category like urban-fantasy.'

Fans were also very vocal about the ending of *Breaking Dawn*.

'Perhaps I'm a bit different, but I really like drama and love dramatic endings, so I would have liked Bella or Edward to die. Probably I would have been sadder if Edward died, so I would have preferred it to be Edward. It annoys me when everything ends up perfect at the end of a series and, unfortunately, that was the case with Bella and Edward. They defeat their enemies, can be together forever, Bella still gets to have contact with her family, Renesmee will live forever as well. It couldn't be any more perfect and in my opinion that ruins the whole book.'

'I thought the whole fourth book was unsuccessful. In becoming a vampire, Bella loses the character traits we loved – she's not clumsy and doesn't go red in uncomfortable situations. She's not a normal woman any more but becomes instead a beautiful, perfect vampire. Even Edward loses his central appeal – he doesn't have to control himself in Bella's presence any more, there's no more inner conflict. He's no longer as threatening as he once seemed. And Jacob, once so in love with Bella, imprints on Renesmee, Bella's child. That makes him lose his entire character. I have to say, sadly, I really didn't like the fourth book. Sorry.'

'I'm happy for them; they deserve the happy end they get, their love, and that it will be forever.'

'I think the ending Stephenie Meyer writes in book four is really nice. It needed a little bit of getting used to, but after thinking about it for a while, I really liked it.'

'It would have been better if Edward could have become mortal for her – so that they could live a normal life together. But the main thing at the end is that they can be together, no matter as what or how.'

'". . . and they lived happily ever after . . ." Can you have a more perfect ending?'

A–Z
OF
KEYWORDS

ALCOHOL

Alcohol makes only a rare appearance in the *Twilight* series. This is probably to do with the fact that Stephenie Meyer is a Mormon (alcohol, coffee and nicotine are not allowed) and also because she loves cars (driving a lot and fast is much safer without alcohol). Alcohol tends to be portrayed in a negative light, as in Bella's opinion that alcohol and other drugs only ever have a bad effect on people, and in Rosalie's story about her fiancé, who preferred hard liquor to champagne and raped her while drunk.

Alcohol isn't mentioned in relation to the vampires, but their favourite drink is so well known and of such significance that any other fluids are unimportant in comparison.

AGE

In the *Twilight* saga, age is important – not only because the story is about teenagers in love but also because vampires never age and werewolves age in a way peculiar to them; they only start to grow old when they stop phasing into wolves. Bella finds it totally unfair that Edward and Jacob stay young, while she grows older with every passing day. This leads to a massive temper tantrum on Bella's part, when she even stamps her foot, echoing Charlie's tirades.

Rosalie succeeds in making the ageing issue clear. She describes how she wishes she could have Emmett grey-haired beside her, with a horde of grandchildren around them. Although that does give Bella something to think about, she still wants to be changed so that time will stand still for her too.

In the end, it's Edward who dispels her worries about friends and relations ageing around her. It gets easier with time, he explains soothingly – after a few decades they all pass away and it's no longer a problem.

Bad Language

Generally there's a very civilised linguistic atmosphere in the *Twilight* saga. The only times this slips is when the werewolves get angry at the vampires, and vice versa; Jacob speaking, for example, of bloodsuckers or leeches, while Edward refers to them as dogs or mongrels. Edward calls Jacob a bastard (which has since become a favoured swear word for *Twilight* fans).

Beauty

Bella has quite precise ideas of beauty. Her ideal of male beauty is without question embodied in Edward, while Alice or Tanya fulfil her ideals of female beauty. An example of a significantly less attractive female is Kim: Bella describes her as having a 'wide' face and eyes too small to detract from the prominent cheek bones.

The theme of beauty is also seen in the story of Rosalie, who's particularly beautiful. Looking back, she sees herself as foolish and superficial and her beauty as being the cause of her misfortune. Rosalie experiences beauty as a curse, although she doesn't wish herself ugly, but simply ordinary.

Bite

A vampire bite is concentrated erotic fantasy, a longing for a dominant creature who will take responsibility, decide what's going to happen and drag its victim away with it. That's why Bella is so keen to give herself up to Edward's authority, to make herself subject to him. The vampire bite and the pain it causes are part of the sexual tension, heightening desire and leading to a symbiosis, merging two beings into one. The vampire bite, the piercing wound initiating change is a literally incisive experience, leading to crossing over into a new way of life. For the person being bitten, this might alternatively mean that they're simply a victim, a donator of life-energy for the biter.

For Bella, both the bite and the change are quite surprising, and quite different to the way the reader and she expected. An injection of vampire venom direct to the heart – delivered by her beloved, at least – lead to a totally non-erotic change for Bella but marks the beginning of a time of safety around Edward.

Blood

To Bella it smells unpleasantly like rust and salt. Whenever she sees and smells it, she becomes dizzy and sometimes faints. That changes during her pregnancy in *Breaking Dawn*, when she develops quite a taste for it, drinking litres of it. No wonder: in all cultures of the world, blood is considered the essence of vitality. Even today some hunters like to drink the blood of their kill. The soul and the strength of the prey is believed to be passed on to the hunter in this way.

Change

Bella wants nothing as much as she wants to be changed into a vampire so that she can be with Edward forever. If she isn't changed, she'll grow older while he stays the same and their love would have to come to an end. One obstacle to this is Edward himself, who is torn. He knows how precious it is to be human. Rosalie reinforces this by wishing she could be human again. She's jealous of Bella and simply can't understand why she wants to become a vampire. Other obstacles are Renée and Charlie – how could she ever make them understand? And how would Jacob react – he would know immediately. His potential disgust keeps casting a shadow over all her blissful plans.

Numerous transformtions of humans into vampires are described, including Carlisle's in book one and Rosalie's in book three and, of course, the highpoint is Bella's change in book four. But Bella's near death experience at the end of book one also features the extreme pain caused when vampire poison gets into the blood.

CONFLICT

There are many conflicts in the *Twilight* saga. The most significant of these is between the vampires and the werewolves. At the beginning it seems impossible to solve, but Bella's persistence and a common enemy succeed in building trust between the groups. By the end of *Eclipse*, Edward, the vampire, and Seth, the werewolf, have even become good friends, foreshadowing greater allegiances in *Breaking Dawn*.

CURIOSITY

Since both vampires and werewolves have to keep their identity secret from humans, there is a ribbon of constant tension running through the saga, as we wonder who might become aware of this double life and when. A variety of signs – unusual behaviour from the vampires and werewolves – make other characters curious in very different ways. Bella draws distinctions here: she likes talking to Angela, even when she asks about Edward because Bella knows she's not simply looking for gossip, like Jessica, but is genuinely interested in Bella's issues.

DANGER

When danger threatens, vampires and werewolves react in a similar way: eyes wide open, nostrils flared, teeth bared. Danger is the theme in the preface to each of the four books.

DREAMS

Dreams play an important role in the *Twilight* saga, which had its own beginnings in Stephenie Meyer's now legendary dream of June 2nd, 2003, when she saw Bella and Edward in a clearing. In the first nightmare Bella describes, she is in the forest with Jacob. He phases into a red-brown wolf with black eyes. Enter Edward, who waves Bella over to him. The wolf is about to attack Edward – and at that moment Bella wakes up. And there it is, the love-triangle story on a plate.

EMANCIPATION

The image of female and male roles conveyed in the *Twilight* saga is the subject of much discussion. The fact that readers can't seem to agree about it suggests that Stephenie Meyer has portrayed a variety of gender relationships without coming down in favour of one particular type. Added to this is the fact that Bella changes during the course of the saga. In the beginning she seems naïve: an inexperienced, self-doubting girl who meets a divinely beautiful, clever, rich and dominant prince. Bella accepts a lot and Edward enjoys the role of protector, which shows him up on a number of occasions as a potential macho chauvinist. But over the course of time, Bella reveals some strengths of her own. For example, when she has to escape from James, she shows herself to be Edward's intellectual superior. In their compromising about the prom and visiting La Push she proves herself tenacious and cunning. Bella's qualities become increasingly apparent, even to managing to escape the watchful eye of her vampire guards, despite the fact that they are superior to her in every way. Bella focuses on her aims with great perseverance and steadfastness. The deeper she gets into the world of vampires and werewolves, the more critical her questions become. When Jacob tries to explain the phenomenon of imprinting, Bella instantly asks about the woman's say in the matter.

FACTS OF LIFE

When Charlie realises at the beginning of *Eclipse* that his eighteen year-old daughter Bella is seriously in love with Edward, he tries to explain the facts of life to her. It's an extremely embarrassing situation for them both. To calm her father down, Bella finally tells him she's still a virgin. Contraception is never mentioned, neither in discussion with her father nor with Edward. The theory is that vampires are infertile, even in cross-over-sex with a human. At the beginning of *Breaking Dawn*, however, Bella becomes pregnant with Edward's child. Teenagers in love really can't be too careful.

FOREST

Many critical scenes of the *Twilight* saga are played out in the forest. Since ancient times forests have been considered – from a modern point of view – a refuge for authors tending to the romantic; as a place where man and nature are at one.

FAMILY

The entire *Twilight* series can be read as a story of longing which ends in a happy family, something Bella's wanted since childhood. As a child of divorce – pulled between Renée and Charlie, Phoenix and Forks, the sun and the rain – Bella as a teenager now experiences similar feelings of division as she is pulled back and forth between vampires and werewolves, between Edward and Jacob. Armed with the requisite will of iron, this young woman now battles for a community which will successfully link the three groups – humans, vampires and werewolves. The *Twilight* series brings these three extremes together in unity, not forgetting a physical in-between link in Renesmee. Hopefully future novels from Stephenie will show whether Renesmee, half vampire, half human with vampire parents and a werewolf who has imprinted on her, might not be the perfect being of the future.

FRIENDS

Bella can't always tell whether Jacob is her friend or her enemy. All she knows for certain is that Edward is far more than a friend. It's only after they've sorted out all the misunderstandings that she realises Jacob means more to her than just a friend, but in a different way to Edward. Bella struggles constantly with the line between lover and friend. Although for Edward, naturally, the term 'lover' would not say enough.

Games

Whenever there's a thunderstorm, the Cullens like to play their version of baseball. The field is huge, somewhere deep in the forest. The pitcher and striker stand a very long way apart and no one wears gloves. When the striker hits the ball, there is an enormously loud, thundering sound – which is why the Cullens have to play their game during storms – luckily Alice can predict the weather more accurately than a meteorologist. Bella is immediately quite sure that she will be bored to death if she ever has to watch another normal major league game.

Another game which features dramatically in the *Twilight* saga is chess. Alice and Edward play chess, yet since each of them can see the move the other is going to make, the pieces are only actually moved at the beginning of the game. The main game is played in their heads.

Stephenie loves the chess metaphor and suggested the cover illustration for book four, because at the end of the story – like in a chess game – the power struggle is not physical, but mental.

Genre

Science-fiction, mystery thriller or horror story? There is a constant stream of discussion linking Stephenie's *Twilight* saga with a range of literary genres. This emphasises just how original it is.

GOOD AND EVIL

In an early scene, Edward asks Bella how she can be so sure that he's some kind of good-natured superhero. How could she think that when she knows he might be dangerous. Is there such a thing as good danger? Could Edward be an evil hero?

Bella is soon confident of her opinion, but distinguishing good from evil is shown to be a constant process in the *Twilight* saga. Even though *Twilight* shows that the Cullens and Jacob are good, subsequent books open this question up further. They aren't all good nor have they always been good. Think of the revenge Rosalie exacts. New questions arise: do they only ever cause harm accidentally or is it sometimes intentional? What about Sam, who damages Emily's beautiful face because he phased into a wolf too close to her? And Edward's disappearance, which leads Bella to contemplate suicide? The reader must question the morality and the motivation behind each character's actions.

Bella finds it hard to understand why there is evil in the world. Why is it that the devilish James and Victoria follow their murderous desires when they could live like the Cullens? In a scene paralleling Rosalie's history, why do the four men who threaten Bella behave the way they do? Why have these four men become what they are? Even the Volturi, who function as vampire police, forcibly ensuring order, threaten and torture Bella and Edward, so Bella is surprised to find that Jasper in particular is generally grateful to them and holds them in high regard, seeing them as the good guys.

Grinning

There is a lot of grinning in the *Twilight* series. But there isn't a grin which creates more tension than Jacob's facial expression when he meets Bella for the third time in his wolf form. At first it seems like this meeting will be horrific for Bella. Jacob the wolf opens his jaws, bares his teeth and generally looks fearsome. But Bella notices his tongue is hanging out of the side of his mouth. She thinks he's grinning, so she giggles, and Jacob's grin grows yet broader. The reader breathes out and realises that from now on Bella will feel at home with the huge wolf, will play with his shaggy fur and make herself comfortable cuddled up against him.

Grounding

Charlie grounds Bella in *Eclipse*, giving her a relatively light sentence for having disappeared for three days without explanation and jumped off a cliff. He hands out the second, stricter sentence after she's secretly been out on a motorcycle with Jacob.

Bella accepts her father's punishments without much complaint, perhaps because Edward is secretly spending almost every night in her room. She plays with the idea of moving out, but reasons against it, thinking that she deserves the punishment and that there will soon be a very long separation from Charlie. Also, being grounded, as well as romantic love, is part of the traditional value system Stephenie Meyer conveys in her *Twilight* saga and which finds such a positive resonance amongst young female readers across the globe. This reveals a longing for strict rules and traditions in a society where an anything goes attitude is often the norm.

HAPPINESS

Happiness is a central theme in the *Twilight* series. Bella's quite convinced that by being changed into a vampire, which will enable her to be with Edward forever, she will find perfect happiness. As a result, she's particularly observant of other people's search for happiness, including other vampires', such as Rosalie. Her fate is particularly moving because, at eighteen years of age, in the 1930s, she believed she had found perfect happiness: Rosalie, so perfect she'd never felt jealousy, was to marry a rich, handsome young man. Shortly before their wedding, however, he raped her while he was drunk. Since then Rosalie has been unhappy. She is jealous of humans, particularly Bella, and tries to persuade her that becoming a vampire will not make her happy. But Bella doesn't believe her.

The exact nature of happiness is a question which crops up in numerous small scenes. For example, in book one, Edward thinks it would be a relief to have told Bella about his secret life, if she knew everything about him. After all, Bella is the first and only human he has ever confided in. When she visits after his great confession, however, he finds that he is not only relieved, but that complete candour makes him actually happy.

Harmony

The entire *Twilight* saga can be seen as a metaphor of international harmony. The need to recognise and respect the diversity of qualities found in the different species in the story is a strong and recurring theme of the books. Again and again there is a risk of war breaking out between the species, but each time it is avoided, and this is largely down to Bella. She fights tirelessly for tolerance. In countless conversations she builds up the vampires' confidence in the werewolves and vice versa. She moves back and forth between the fronts, always looking for the bigger picture until finally the opponents themselves see a different perspective and change their attitudes. This result of her massive peace effort can only be admired by the reader. And even when Bella's negotiation skills are exhausted, chance usually steps in to help in the form of a common enemy, such as Victoria.

Hemlock Pine

A huge forest begins just behind the garden of Charlie's house in Forks. Among other types of tree, maple and yews grow there. A lesser known variety is the Hemlock pine: it is evergreen and can live up to a thousand years – almost like a vampire.

HISTORY

Jasper Cullen mentions an intervention by the Volturi in Mexico after the number of dead in a vampire war had reached epidemic proportions. This was, he says, an unforgettable chapter in the history of the immortals. Vampires, according to Jasper, have a history just like humans do. What human history recorded as a plague was often actually the result of vampire wars – it's just that not many survive to tell the tale. It would be very interesting to read a chronicle of vampire history, a book to tell the story of historic events from a vampire point of view.

HUNTERS

The vampire James is a perfect hunter, a tracker who never gives up until he has found his victim, sucked their blood dry and killed them. James's partner, Victoria, is not as focused or talented as he is, but she also never gives up: in the face of the Cullens' and the werewolves' near-perfect defence system around Bella, she takes drastic measures, creating an army of young vampires who devastate Seattle during the period leading up to the battle.

IMMORTALITY

Bella insists absolutely that she will exchange her human mortality for vampire immortality. She has only rare moments of doubt, feeling like a lamb being led to the slaughter. But her longing to be with Edward forever fully outweighs all other fears.

IMPRINTING

Some werewolves imprint, suggesting that they have a predestined partner. Like love at first sight, but far more powerful, these werewolves can't help but utterly love that one particular person. In order to imprint, the werewolf has to actually see the female in question, and sometimes the person they imprint on can still be very young. If the age difference is very big, then the affection does not take the form of romantic love – that will come later. The werewolf will first function as a brother, protector or friend. By the end of *Eclipse*, only Sam, Jared and Quil have imprinted, but as *Breaking Dawn* unfolds, the number increases until even Jacob has imprinted – on Renesmee, of all people.

This very odd process is described in detail in *Eclipse*. It stretches the reader's powers of imagination – and sometimes patience – until it becomes clear in *Breaking Dawn* that imprinting helps provide a happy solution to the unhappy relationship triangle between Bella, Edward and Jacob.

Bella tries to explain the marvel of imprinting by comparing the way Jared looks at Kim to the way a mother looks at her newborn child, or the look of a blind man seeing the sun for the first time. Edward shows how well read he is when he says it reminds him of *A Midsummer Night's Dream*, where magic confuses everything.

KISSES

The kisses Bella shares with Edward on the one hand and

Jacob on the other are, in accordance with their natures, quite different. Vampire kisses are divinely fascinating, cold and yet fiery. Werewolf kisses are warm, and soft, like human kisses. Lucky Bella gets to enjoy the full spectrum of the most passionate kisses! A purely human kiss, such as Mike could give her, is of absolutely no interest to her.

LIES

Bella is fundamentally open and honest. But her complicated relationship with Edward forces her into frequent white lies. She often tells half-truths and, in fact, when she is being hunted by James, she not only lies to Charlie, but hurts him badly by using the same words that her mother used when she left him.

LOVE

Love is the theme of all themes in the *Twilight* saga. When Bella hears that Sam was in love with Leah before falling in love with Emily, she works out that most people fall in love a number of times in their lives. For Bella, Edward is not just the love of her human life. She realises that she will love him for longer, he's the love of her existence – her only love.

And yet, how confusing love can be, even for Bella. This is apparent in her relationship with Jacob, which has a brief moment of actual romance at the end of *Eclipse*. Bella admits to herself that she loves him. This admission is preceded by a kiss of such passion, a kiss of a quality so clearly greater than any previous kisses with Edward. It's hardly surprising: neither Bella nor Jacob have to be careful when they kiss. The kiss goes on and on, lasting longer than any kiss Bella has yet experienced and is so passionate that Bella hasn't the faintest desire to stop it. Even so, Bella decides that the love she feels for him still isn't enough to change anything. Bella quickly justifies her infidelity – Jacob had, after all, just threatened to go into battle against Victoria's young vampires in the hope of an accidental death. The pressure Jacob put her under is also the reason Edward doesn't feel there's anything at all to forgive her for. Bella hates herself anyway for giving in to a moment of pleasurable weakness and she expects to be punished for it. But Edward explains to her that she loves Jacob and that it's right that she does. After all in her moment of greatest need, caused by Edward, it was Jacob who was there to help her.

MARRIAGE

Bella's image of marriage is shaped by the failure of her parents' relationship. Bella considers Renée's decision to marry a man she hardly knew straight out of high school, and then to have Bella barely a year later to have been the biggest mistake of her life. Although Renée insists it was the best thing that ever happened to her, she still begs Bella not to make the same mistakes. She should go to college and get a career before she starts getting into any serious relationships.

This is the reason for Bella's aversion to an early engagement and to marrying Edward. She doesn't want to repeat her mother's mistakes. Apart from that, she's also afraid of Renée's reaction when she tells her she's getting married.

MAGNETS

Magnets are one of Stephenie Meyer's favourite metaphors, to symbolise the attraction and repulsion in relationships between people. Bella's mother, Renée, uses this image. Bella uses the two magnets on her fridge door to represent the opposite pull of the two men she's caught between. She sees the impossibility of bringing the two magnets close together as representing the impossibility of changing the rules of nature – in this case the enmity between vampires and werewolves.

MENUS

Bella wonders how her father could have survived seventeen years almost entirely without using the stove. Renée's failed cooking experiments are infamous and Bella has to earn her father's trust from dish to dish, such as chicken enchiladas (with a lot of chilli and onions). Since Charlie brings home a big fish from time to time, Bella decides to buy a fish cookbook in Seattle. She never makes it to Seattle, however, so she makes do with remembering old recipes. In the end, after watching a cookery programme, she decides she probably doesn't put enough effort into Charlie's food. Amongst other things, she serves him lasagne, defrosted hamburgers or waffles, which she throws in the toaster. Bella can always get on the right side of Charlie when she makes him beef stroganoff according to Grandma Swan's recipe. The culinary high point is Harry Clearwater's homemade herb mix for fresh fish. Interestingly, Bella never uses garlic in her cooking.

Money

Money plays a significant role in the *Twilight* series. At the beginning, Bella's planning to spend her entire savings on an ancient, used car. Luckily Charlie has bought her the Chevy truck. This shows that Bella doesn't exactly live in the lap of luxury. As a policeman in Forks, Charlie doesn't earn that much. The same goes for Renée, a Kindergarten teacher, and her second husband, Phil, who just about manages to make ends meet – whether as a baseball player or trainer. No wonder Bella's better suited to Jacob in attitude and background, since he lives a quite simple life in comparison to Edward for whom money is no object. The gap between wealth and poverty is particularly apparent in a short scene in *Eclipse*: Bella's beloved and ancient motorbike is parked in the Cullens' garage beside a brand spanking new one. The sight of the two bikes together makes Bella sad, because she sees it as a picture of herself compared to Edward.

Morality

When Bella hears that human blood could strengthen the Cullens so much that Victoria's newborns, even with greater numbers, wouldn't stand a chance, she thinks she would, at least theoretically, be prepared to sacrifice human lives. She is shocked at her own thoughts, but to protect Edward, she would stop at nothing. There are many moral dilemmas in the *Twilight* saga and the reader is often forced to decide personally what she or he would or wouldn't find acceptable.

Edward's actions following his change are just such a moment in the story. For the first few years as a vampire, Edward found Carlisle's philosophy of abstinence from human blood very hard to follow.

Edward, being able to read Carlisle's thoughts, knew he was absolutely sincere, valued it and understood why he had come to that decision. So it took about ten years before he defied Carlisle. Edward describes it as a phase of typical teenage rebellion. His anger grew because Carlisle was constantly curbing his appetite.

Edward confesses to Bella that during this period he went his own way and lived as a monster, killing humans. Morally, he justified his actions by saying his ability to read thoughts allowed him to spare, even save, the innocent and hunt and kill evil people. 'If I followed a murderer down a dark alley where he stalked a young girl – if I saved her, then surely I wouldn't be so terrible?'

Edward had his own philosophy and lived by himself as a nomad for about ten years. But he suffered increasingly from a bad conscience. He confesses his mental tortures to Bella: he saw himself more and more as a monster. Slowly his moral attitude changed and he realised it would be wrong for him to continue to take responsibility for everyone, whether he was to save them or they were to quench his thirst. He didn't want to play God any more. So he returned to Esme and Carlisle, who welcomed him back like a prodigal son. Since then he has lived according to Carlisle's principles.

Bella isn't revolted by Edward's past as a murderer. She accepts it because it makes sense to her.

Mortal Danger

Bella's life seems to be in constant danger. On the one hand, she seems to attract accidents to herself as if by magic; on the other hand, her love for Edward creates such a complex situation that a number of vampires, independently and for different reasons, want to kill her – either as revenge or on principle. These threats to her life ensure a constant tension throughout the *Twilight* saga.

Muscles

A man's physique is important to Bella. Edward's marble chest is legendary.

In *Eclipse*, the reader learns why Jacob almost never wears a T-shirt. When phasing into a wolf, clothes don't just disappear, they are ripped to pieces if they're not taken off first! That's why he wears as little as possible, is often barefoot and has a leather band bound around his ankle to tie his clothes to him, where they won't get in the way, so he has them when he phases back to human form. At any rate, when Bella sees his bare chest, she's able to comment on how muscular he has become. She doesn't compare him with Edward, but she is impressed.

Nature

Amongst Stephenie's many descriptions of nature, the wood is most important. What Bella disliked at the beginning grows more and more interesting to her, culminating in the discovery of the forest clearing in the famous *Confessions* chapter: after a long hike through dense undergrowth, Bella says it's the most beautiful place she's ever seen. Suddenly her yearning for the landscape around Phoenix, which until then she has described with longing, has disappeared. The clearing is a circular meadow, filled with wildflowers – purple, yellow and white. A stream bubbles nearby. In the haze the light seems buttery. Perfect conditions for an outing with Edward in the sunlight.

Pack

The reader is given an insight into pack dynamics first through Edward's mind-reading skills and then, in book four, directly through Jacob when he becomes the narrator. The collective pack mind is faced with an individual will when the Alpha male (Sam) is suddenly challenged by the rightful heir to the lead position (Jacob); Leah, the only female wolf in the pack has a real problem standing up to the men, not least because the wolves can read each other's minds when in wolf form. When Edward listens in on the pack's thoughts, he can hear the thoughts of everyone at once since they essentially become one mind.

PETS

When Bella is getting on well with Jacob in his wolf form – partly because he can't talk (and annoy her) – she tells the werewolf, as she cuddles up cosily against him, that she always wanted a dog as a child but couldn't have one because Renée was allergic to dog hair.

PRESENTS

Bella receives many gifts including personal ones, such as the tiny wooden wolf on Jacob's bracelet. That makes Edward jealous, as she never accepts any gifts from him without making a huge fuss – perhaps understandable after the fiasco of her eighteenth birthday party. She soothes the irritated Edward, however, by telling him he's the best present she could want. He has given himself to her, which is far more than she could ever deserve.

PROM NIGHT

Bella refuses to attend the leavers' prom with Edward. She hates this kind of occasion, because she's a bad dancer and detests evening wear.

REALITY

After her first visit to the Cullens' house, Bella feels as if she is returning to reality. But what is reality in the *Twilight* saga? Stephenie has thought everything through so thoroughly that many younger readers of the *Twilight* saga are inclined to join Bella in believing in that world of monsters.

Many readers see the known world as only part of a reality; they think things are in fact far more complex because in secret there really are monsters striking terror into people's hearts.

Everything that it's impossible to explain in everyday life, all the horrific reports in the news could, they say, be explained by the existence of monsters. Serial killers, for example, would really be young vampires out of control. Monstrous occurrences would be caused by actual monsters.

It's not until *Eclipse* that Bella describes her dawning understanding that vampires play a far greater role in the world than she had thought. It gives her goosebumps to think about how populated this 'other world' is, and to think about her own future as a vampire.

Religion

Neither Edward nor Bella can imagine that the world came into existence of its own doing. Tongue-in-cheek, they philosophise that maybe vampires and humans came into existence in the same way that baby seals and killer whales did. On Bella's first visit to the Cullens' house, she's surprised to see a big wooden cross on the wall. It was made in 1630 and hangs there for nostalgic reasons: it once belonged to Carlisle's father. He carved it himself and hung it above the pulpit where he preached. At the beginning of book two, after Jasper's attack on Bella, she and Carlisle have a long talk about religion. Bella explains that she is not religious at all. Carlisle, however, is and tries to explain his faith to her.

Revenge

As in *Wuthering Heights*, revenge in the *Twilight* saga is sweet. Revenge is the motive at the heart of most of the conflicts. Sometimes chains of revenge occur: James – Laurent – Victoria – Irina.

Rivalry

Edward and Jacob are not the only rivals. Bella's other admirers, above all Mike, are also rivals of the two male heroes. Then there's the rivalry between the vampires themselves. And, last but not least, Bella herself has a rival: the beautiful, strawberry-blonde Tanya of the Denali clan. All these relationships spark strong emotions: from jealousy to murderous intent. The *Twilight* saga shows repeatedly how an individual can overcome base desires. In this, too, the series makes the case for tolerance, peace, freedom, friendship and love.

Sacrifice

In her dreams Bella sacrifices herself like the 'third wife' in Quileute legend. So desperate is she to help Edward in the battle between Victoria's newborns and the Cullens, she feels there's no other option but to stab herself to distract the young vampires. Later, when she's awake, she comes to understand and accept her wish to sacrifice herself for the victory of good over evil, for justice and for peace.

Shortly before the decisive battle against Victoria, Jacob and Bella compete as to who will sacrifice themselves. Both are plagued by feelings of guilt and both are prepared to die for the right cause.

Safety

The question of where Bella is safest comes up again and again: at the Cullens' or with the werewolves? Some of the greatest tension in the *Twilight* saga is down to the fact that each side thinks she's only safe with them.

Edward claims werewolves are unpredictable, Jacob claims vampires too dangerous and both sides are partly right. Yet Bella never stops highlighting each side's good points; there's a chronic threat of war and constant peace-brokering, with Bella playing the diplomat moving back and forth between the fronts, attempting to break down prejudice and clear up misunderstandings.

Bella knows more about werewolves than the vampires and vice versa, because she's open to both sides and has the trust of them all.

School

In *Eclipse*, Bella is in her last year of school. Freedom is just around the corner. At the end of high school, students decide if they want to go on to university. Edward wants to better Bella's future by getting her into an elite university, but Bella has other considerations – she likes the idea of Alaska Southeast since the skies over Juneau are cloudy for three hundred and twenty days of the year. But Bella thinks the applications are unnecessary anyway, since she's counting on being changed as soon as school is finished and then, as a young and unpredictable vampire, she would not be able to be around humans until she's developed a dependable degree of self-control. She does allow that she could take on a distance learning degree, and has forever to continue with her studies.

Self–control

Before Bella is changed, the relationship she and Edward have is characterised by self-control. There is a constant danger of loss of control. Intimacy must be cut short since they cannot risk going beyond a certain level of excitement, and unrestricted passion between them would almost certainly be fatal. The *Twilight* saga is almost like an unbelievably long preparatory phase, almost 2,000 pages of it.

Edward can't imagine that Bella could ever be present when he's hunting and with good reason: when he's hunting, Edward stops controlling himself and gives himself up to his senses, in particular his sense of smell. If Bella were near him then, it could end very badly. But there are other types of situations where he gets too close to Bella and his passion could get out of control. That's when he makes the confusing comment: 'I'm only human'. Later in her bedroom, she asks him if he finds her physically attractive, he says yes, by saying, 'I may not be human, but I am a man!'

Carlisle has needed two hundred years to perfect his self-control. He has become almost entirely immune to the allure of human blood and practises medicine without being tempted at all.

There are at least two ways in which Edward could lose his self-control; one of these Bella despises, the other she longs for. On numerous occasions Edward threatens to lose control and kill Jacob. More frequently, when he's very close to Bella, he nearly loses control, which could kill her by accident. Luckily, in *Breaking Dawn*, during their first night of lovemaking, he only causes her multiple bruises and otherwise it's just pillows and a bed-frame that get damaged. But Bella only realises all this the following morning.

Selfishness

Bella is surprised when she finds out that Edward thinks he would be being selfish if he allowed her to be changed. She thought he'd be against it because, as a vampire, she wouldn't have her warmth or her scent and he might not find her so attractive. Edward admits that he will miss her heartbeat, the most important sound to him, but that she will still be his Bella, just a little more hard-wearing.

Silver Moon

The scar that a vampire bite leaves behind looks like an elegant crescent moon, and, in the right light, like a silvery moon.

Soul

Whether or not the Cullens have a soul is a point not even they themselves are clear on. Bella, on the other hand, is absolutely convinced that they do and that they are good.

Suicide

Some of the characters in the *Twilight* saga are so desperate about life that they feel suicide is the only possible path left to them. The theme of suicide runs through Bella's story: her mother-in-law leaped to her death. Edward decided to kill himself when he heard of Bella's supposed death. The 'third wife' in Quileute legend takes her own life during a battle between the werewolves and vampires to save her family and whole tribe. During a battle the werewolves can't possible win, she throws herself at the feet of a female vampire and stabs herself to distract their attention and lay herself open to attack. Not least, Bella herself toys with the thought of suicide more than once when Edward leaves her (in book two); and she decides to sacrifice herself like the 'third wife' in the battle against Victoria's newborns.

Superheroes

In the fifth chapter of *Twilight* Bella admits that she has come up with a theory behind Edward's abilities – that he must have been bitten by a radioactive spider, like Peter Parker, aka Spider-Man. Given Edward's opulent lifestyle, it would make Edward a supernatural being somewhere between Peter Parker and Bruce Wayne, the millionaire alter ego of Batman. But Edward refuses to see himself as such, suggesting instead that he might be 'the bad guy'.

TEARS

When Edward finishes playing the piano for her, Bella has tears in her eyes from the sheer melancholy of the last chords. Edward touches the corner of her eye, catching a tear, looks at it carefully and finally licks his finger. Since he himself can't cry any more, one of Bella's tears is almost as precious as a drop of her blood.

TEMPERATURE

Cold – inherent to vampires – and heat – inherent to werewolves – are constantly present themes. Temperature variations become especially interesting in extreme situations, such as in moments of intimacy. So Edward's cold hands make Bella feel warm and, when cuddled up to him, Bella melts into his cold chest.

THOUGHTS

Thoughts don't tend to be a private matter in the *Twilight* saga. Since werewolves can hear the thoughts of their own kind and Edward can hear most people's thoughts, communication is much more complex than in other novels. Stephenie uses telepathy masterfully to heighten dramatic effect. One of the arguments between Edward and Jacob illustrates this perfectly: the vampire reads Jacob's mind, while Jacob is deliberately concentrating his thoughts on how utterly destroyed Bella was when Sam found her in the woods – knowledge Jacob only has because he saw it in Sam's thoughts when they were in wolf form. Jacob can use these thoughts to torture Edward, because Edward is fully aware that Bella's suffering was the result of his leaving her.

Time

Bella has the feeling that time in Forks passes at different speeds. Sometimes whole weeks pass in a blur. Sometimes every second is important.

Additionally, time is an important narrative tool for creating and maintaining tension. An example is in *Eclipse*, when Jacob believes he's got a few years before Bella is expecting to be changed and she corrects him. It's a matter of weeks, she tells him. This sudden lack of time intensifies the situation in a number of ways. After all, Edward is and will continue to remain seventeen, while every passing day brings Bella closer to her nineteenth birthday.

Treaty Line

There is an invisible Vampire-Werewolf Treaty Line that runs between Forks and La Push. It is a demarcation line between war zones, between vampire and Quileute territory, but during the course of the story it becomes less and less important.

TWILIGHT

The title given to the first book, which Stephenie wasn't happy with at first, but which has in fact become the title for the entire saga. Looking at the various title translations of *Twilight* in other languages, it's easy to see how difficult it would be to find a suitable title for a first book. The German is *Bite at Dawn*, in Finland it becomes *Temptation*, in France *Fascination*, and in Japan – where the book was divided into three – it is: *The Boy I Love Is a Vampire*, *Blood Tastes of Sadness*, and *The Vampire Family in Darkness*.

UNIQUENESS

Bella is the only character in the *Twilight* series to have free choice about becoming something other than human. None of the other vampires or werewolves were able to make a choice about their supernatural or unnatural existence. They're forced to become what they are. Some of them accept it, some feel uncomfortable with themselves and are envious of normal humans.

VAMPIRES

Vampires are also known as blood drinkers, leeches or the cold ones in the *Twilight* books. There is a long vampire tradition and, unlike many other fantasy creatures, vampires are enjoying a particular boom – this is thanks in particular to Stephenie, but also to Anne Rice, Darren Shan and *Buffy the Vampire Slayer*. Today's vampires have evolved a long way from their forbears. Vampires first seemed to be mentioned in the Middle Ages as horrific beings, scapegoats for plagues. Over the centuries, the way people imagine their characteristics and appearance has been gradually changing. The *Twilight* vampire – like many of their predecessors – is a direct descendant of Lord Ruthven, created in 1816 by Dr John W. Polidori. Ruthven displays a number of the same features as a Cullen: a pale face, an extraordinary look in his eyes, the slightly arrogant manner of a beautiful and elitist eccentric, well off, slightly melancholy, slightly bored and cool, like Robert Pattinson in sunglasses.

The Cullen vampires are less like Bram Stoker's famous creation, Count Dracula, but the various vampire myths across the centuries do have a few important elements in common. Vampires are contagious – they're able to create new vampires, usually through a bite or sharing of blood, and now uniquely in less bloody fashion according to *Breaking Dawn*. The other common element is their immortality, with the result that some become tired of living. These experience living as a duty, a burden and are trying to find release somehow. Suicide, as Carlisle Cullen found, isn't possible for them, which makes the whole undertaking far more difficult. One option is to break the Volturi's carefully protected laws so seriously that they simply destroy the criminal, which can happen in a flash even to vampires as extraordinarily cunning as Victoria. It's another consistent element of vampire mythology is that the one sure way to kill a vampire is to tear them up and burn the pieces.

So what is it about vampires, and especially Stephenie's Cullens, that makes them so attractive to young people? There are perhaps similarities to be found between the mentality of vampires and young people: both exist at the outer edges of convention, both turn night into day, they rebel against stubborn, conservative people, reject stillness, are constantly in motion, restless and sleepless, searching for the next new thing, the next fashion, the next kick, preferably out at night, preferably cool – literally too, pale, thirsty, having yet to find their place in society.

VIOLENCE

Nobody in Stephenie Meyer's *Twilight* saga is so dead-set against violence as Carlisle Cullen. But, towards the end of *Eclipse*, when Victoria's army of newborns threatens the very existence of the Cullens, Carlisle charges his foster son Jasper with the task of teaching them all how best to kill young vampires. Stephenie describes the threat in epic proportions, showing how even the dedicated pacifist Carlisle can be turned into a warrior if his family and way of life are threatened.

WEDDING

For a long time, Bella is resistant to Edward's wish to marry her before she's changed into a vampire. Bella says she'd feel like a small town slut who lets her boyfriend get her pregnant straight out of high school and then has to marry him. But

Edward remains firm. He still believes in the romantic notions of his own human age and wants to do things the right way: first the wedding, then sex. Not the other way around, as Bella so desperately wants.

Werewolves

A creature somewhere between human and animal, between man and wolf. Female werewolves are rare, but Stephenie brings a female wolf into the Quileute pack to fabulous effect. Ever since Zeus changed King Lycaon into a wolf, this creature has been one of the most fascinating elements of horror stories. Like the Cullens, the members of the Quileute tribe are highly evolved. Characterised by a humanistic view of the world their highest commandment, second only to self-preservation, is brotherly love. Not only does Jacob have a soul and a conscience, he would also never kill another human being, whereas Edward had to relearn this morality. Edward and Jacob would both give their life to save Bella's. So neither Stephenie's werewolves nor the Cullen vampires could really be termed monsters, and with their ability to imprint, the werewolves can even be seen as embodying a new ideal of perfect and fateful love.

In popular belief, werewolves and vampires had some traits in common, such as being active at night and attacking humans. In contrast to vampires, a werewolf was not so hard to hurt or kill. At some times, and in some places, such as Eastern Europe, werewolves and vampires have even become the same creature in myth.

✦

THE TWILIGHT FACTFILES
STEPHENIE MEYER'S LIFE

Stephenie Meyer was born Stephenie Morgan on December 24th, 1973 in Hartford, Connecticut. In our interview she did confirm that she does celebrate a *Twilight* day at Christmas, although there's nothing about that to be found on her site. She doesn't confirm the rumours that she grew up in straitened circumstances and was in receipt of benefits until just before the publication of *Twilight*.

Her unusual first name was given to her by her father, who added the '-ie' ending to his own name just for her. Stephenie doesn't find her name a burden, although before her *Twilight* success, she had to spell her name in all sorts of situations to uncomprehending hotel receptionists and officials. On the other hand, Stephenie points out, thanks to the quirky spelling of her first name, it's easy to Google her. On her own website, she signs her articles Steph, keeping a closeness to Seth, her brother, who writes most of the articles on the website.

Stephenie grew up in Phoenix, Arizona with five brothers and sisters, Seth, Emily, Jacob, Paul and Heidi. She attended Chapparal High School in Scottsdale, Arizona and Brigham Young University in Provo, Utah, where she completed her English degree in 1995.

She met Christian, known as 'Pancho', in Arizona when she was still a child. He later became her husband. They got married in 1994 and have three sons together: Gabe, Seth and Eli.

She calls the *Twilight* experience, which has changed her whole life, a 'rollercoaster ride without safety belts'. At any rate she's glad it's really shown her co-students, who all prophesied a career in fast food outlets given her choice of subject. Stephenie is now a multi-millionaire. Her father, a businessman, keeps the accounts and checks the contracts.

With a heavy heart, Stephenie has recently had to pass on the task of answering fan-mail to a secretary. Since her three sons have been attending school and kindergarten in the mornings, she has had more time to dedicate to her writing.

LITERATURE AND RELIGION

Stephenie's favourite authors who have had the most important influence on her writing are (in no particular order) Orson Scott Card, Jane Austen, William Shakespeare, Maeve Binchy, the Brontë sisters, Daphne du Maurier, L.M. Montgomery, Louisa May Alcott, Eva Ibbotson, William Goldman, Douglas Adams and Janet Evanovich. Orson Scott

Card is by far and away the least well-known of the names she mentions, but he uses some of his books to voice his Mormon traditions. He has published science-fiction, fantasy, horror stories and thrillers.

Stephenie makes no secret of her religion either – she's probably the best known Mormon in the world. She says her faith is very important to her and she tries to live by its teachings, although she says she's not a good example of a Mormon. But she still wants to be the best person she can be and in those terms maybe she can be seen as a good example. Even after *Breaking Dawn* was published, she was still emphasising that she never consciously brings religion into her books, and wasn't trying to push any kind of message in her *Twilight* series. She writes because writing makes her feel good and happy. If there are religious elements to be found in the books, then it was subconscious.

✦

THE TWILIGHT STORY

Stephenie's dream launched the *Twilight* saga. She dreamt of a young woman in a forest clearing; a vampire is in love with her, but he also thirsts for her blood. The dream was so vivid that Stephenie, then a housewife and mother of three young sons, wrote it down the very next morning. Just three months later the dream had become her first novel. Anyone who reads the end of *Twilight* carefully might be forgiven for thinking it's the end of the story. Edward's keen on Bella, who wants to be bitten and the reader doesn't know as he kisses her on the neck if that's what he's about to do. Stephenie reports that she did originally plan it as a stand-alone novel, a one-off, without any real hope that it would make her an author.

Stephenie sent the first manuscripts to friends and family in homemade envelopes. The response, especially from her sister, was so overwhelmingly positive that she began to think of publishing it under the pseudonym Morgan Meyer.

Stephenie quickly found a literary agent, who was able to stir up interest with a number of publishers. The publisher they accepted paid $750,000 for a three-book deal, a high figure for a debut novel. But everybody hoped that, with the help of two further volumes, the trilogy would be a success. And they were right. At the moment it's a quartet – it says 'the end' at the end of the fourth volume – but the fans are clamouring for spin-offs and Stephenie herself keeps mentioning possibilities.

About 70 million copies of the *Twilight* novels have been sold worldwide, and they are published in thirty-seven countries.

BOOK ONE: TWILIGHT

This is the story of seventeen year-old Bella Swan, who, with a heavy heart, leaves sunny Phoenix, her mother Renée and step-father Phil to move to the rainy town of Forks. Her father, who works as a policeman there, lives alone in a small house on the edge of the forest. Bella finds it hard getting used to the bad weather and her new life. She quickly attracts a number of male admirers at her high school, but the boy she's interested in appears to find her repulsive – seventeen year-old Edward's behaviour is inexplicably peculiar. When he saves Bella's life using what can only be supernatural powers, she guesses he might be a vampire. She feels such a strong attraction for him that she overcomes all fear. Bella wants him not just to kiss her but also to bite her, so that she and Edward can stay young and together forever.

But Edward has reservations about changing her which are put on hold by the arrival of three nomadic vampires which threaten Bella and the people she cares about most.

BOOK TWO: NEW MOON

This is the story of how Bella and Edward, despite being such a dissimilar couple, manage to make life work for them. A happy future seems to be stretching out before them, but on Bella's eighteenth birthday, which they celebrate at the Cullens' house, she cuts herself on a piece of wrapping paper while unpacking a gift. One little drop of blood is enough to cause total chaos, during which Bella loses a lot of blood. All the Cullens except Carlisle have to leave the house in a hurry. Edward decides to break it off permanently, and all the Cullens leave Forks to put Bella out of the constant danger of losing her life. Bella grieves for a long time, but later begins to spend time with Jacob and finds she enjoys it, despite discovering that he is part of the Quileute werewolf pack who are the traditional enemies of all vampires. However, they are therefore able to protect her when Laurent returns.

Bella also discovers that she can hear Edward's voice whenever she puts herself in danger. Bella thinks of more and more reckless activities in order to hear his voice. In this way, she gets close to committing suicide and nearly does die jumping off the cliffs into the sea. In the moment of greatest danger, she feels the greatest happiness. Jacob rescues Bella, but just as new happiness seems to be opening up for Bella, it's shattered by the news that Edward is in mortal danger and she's the only one who can save him.

BOOK THREE: ECLIPSE

In this book Edward and Bella are planning their future together. They still haven't agreed as to whether they'll marry before Bella's changed – as the more traditional Edward wants – or whether Bella should be changed straightaway and the wedding – which Bella hates the thought of – be put on hold. Meanwhile, a serial murderer is on the rampage in Seattle. Edward, however, thinks it's actually a vampire. The threat moves ever closer: some of Bella's clothes disappear from her bedroom. Clearly there are young vampires on the loose, who could be dangerous to the Cullens as well as Bella. Bella's clear affection for Jacob is also causing problems. Untiringly Bella tries to encourage understanding between the werewolves and the vampires. It's the danger from Seattle that finally unites the two sides in a battle against evil.

BOOK FOUR: BREAKING DAWN

This tells the story of how Bella decides Edward's the one she really loves, but won't give up her friendship with Jacob. But Jacob can't bear the thought of her becoming a vampire and turns away from his friend once again. After a glittering wedding at the Cullens' house and a fantastic honeymoon off the coast of Brazil, Bella realises she's pregnant and Edward's the only possible father. This is a first for everybody, including Carlisle. The pregnancy develops at an incredible speed – in just a few weeks it ends in a bloody and painful birth, and Bella is changed into a vampire. Carefully she feels her way into her new life as a vampire and gets used to her speedily developing daughter, Renesmee. The Volturi hear about the child and threaten the Cullens. Instead of a battle there's a psychic clash, during which Bella discovers that she can use her mental shield in ever greater ways, enabling her to protect not only herself but also those who are dear to her from telepathic attack. Like a game of chess, the clash ends in a stalemate, bringing a happy end for all the protagonists, even Jacob, who has imprinted on Renesmee.

Many readers are annoyed by the plot in book four; they don't understand why a story about teenagers develops into a story about marriage, pregnancy and birth. Stephenie's response is that she sees it as realistic development. Life changes, the world changes. Children grow up.

FOREVER DAWN AND OTHER BOOKS

Stephenie used the name Stephenie Morgan Meyer for the manuscript of *Forever Dawn*. She wrote this book as a sequel to the debut book, *Twilight* and it was one of three epilogues to *Twilight*. Stephenie was quite far into writing by the time it was clear that *Twilight* was to be categorised as a children's book. *Forever Dawn* will never be published, partly because Stephenie doesn't think it's good enough, partly because it's too 'adult'. Looking back, she sees it simply as practice for *New Moon*, as a trial run. It also contains elements of

Breaking Dawn, which really is more adult. *Forever Dawn* became a quite unique birthday present for Stephenie's older sister. An index of chapters and a cover painted by Stephenie herself can be found on the internet.

Midnight Sun, however, may well see the light of day. *Midnight Sun*, the story of the first book told from Edward's perspective was to have been published as a continuation of the story after the fourth book of the *Twilight* series. However, because the first twelve chapters of the original manuscript were posted illegally on the internet, Stephenie gave up further work on the book and published the first twelve chapters on her own website. It's not yet clear what direction *Midnight Sun* will take. But Stephenie has given readers hope that she might continue work on the manuscript once she has enough distance to the distressing incident.

Stephenie has also promised *The Twilight Saga: The Official Guide*, which is to reveal further details and background knowledge about the Cullens and other *Twilight* characters. She also revealed that she might be thinking about writing sequels from other characters' points of view. On the other hand, her adult novel *The Host* has also enjoyed success to the extent that she is now thinking of writing sequels to that. Working titles for these books have already been decided on: *The Soul* and *The Seeker*. Stephenie has spoken of numerous ideas for further books, such as a ghost story *Summer House* and a time travel story which hasn't yet got a title.

In 2007 a story by Stephenie had already appeared in an anthology called *Prom Nights from Hell*.

✦

CHARACTERS

In the previous chapters we have concentrated primarily on Isabella Swan and Edward Cullen. In this section we'll look at some further character points which haven't yet been discussed and also at the main characters in order of appearance. This arrangement almost automatically forms the following groupings: the Swans, the Cullens, the Quileute and the Volturi, followed by minor characters.

Isabella Swan

She's the main character in the *Twilight* saga. With only a few exceptions, the reader sees the story through her eyes. Isabella, known as Bella, the first person narrator of this extraordinary story, was born on September 13th (additional information suggests 1987). So Bella is a virgo, the sign of the virgin and there are many allusions to her actually being a virgin too – until *Breaking Dawn*. At the beginning of the *Twilight* saga she's seventeen, and by the end of book four she's reached nineteen. And after she's been changed into a vampire, she'll remain this age for all eternity.

Bella's an only child, daughter of Renée and Charlie, born in Forks. Bella's parents separate when she's about six months old. Renée can't bear living in rainy Forks any more and takes Bella to live with her in Phoenix. Charlie stays behind in Forks, alone, and Bella visits him in the summer holidays. When Renée marries Phil Dwyer, Bella is seventeen and worries that she'll be in their way. She moves to live with her father in Forks of her own free will but without much hope of being happy. That's where the *Twilight* saga begins, the starting point for Bella's love of Edward Cullen, the vampire and her friendship with Jacob Black, the werewolf.

Bella has pale skin, brown eyes and long brown hair. She can't bear the sight of blood and she's fascinated by beauty. At the beginning she says of the Cullens she can't imagine any door would stay closed to that much beauty. Which, she decides, means they must want the isolation they live in.

Bella doesn't have a particular favourite colour. It changes every day. She does, however, have a favourite semi-precious stone. For a long time it was garnet. But since she met Edward it's been topaz, because it makes her think of his eyes.

Fashion is of no interest to Bella. She usually wears jeans, often with a polo-neck jumper. Even in summer, jeans and a T-shirt is her favourite outfit. Alice Cullen is constantly trying to change this. Bella's thinks back fondly to the spaghetti straps and shorts she could wear when she lived in Phoenix. When she visits the vampire family for the first time, she puts on her only skirt. It's long and pale brown. She wears a dark blue blouse with it and puts her hair up in a ponytail.

Bella insists she doesn't care whether Edward is human or 'a monster'. Between Jacob and Edward, Bella sees herself as neutral. 'I am Switzerland,' she says. She considers Forks to be a neutral area as well. She tries, tirelessly, to end the enmity between the vampires and the werewolves.

Bella's not exactly rolling in money the way the Cullens are, so she has a part-time job at Newton's Olympic Outfitters.

Bella's convinced that men are moody when they're hungry. Food plays an important role, even though Bella only sees herself as being an average cook.

Bella changes over the course of the *Twilight* saga, and not just in that she becomes an un-dead mother! There are many smaller changes along the way: for example, in *Eclipse* she sits quite still when she's nervous. She's picked up this reaction to worrying news from Edward.

Bella's two most obvious characteristics change too: after being transformed, her clumsiness is forever a thing of the past. She becomes a vampire equipped with supernatural powers. Her talent, having a mind others cannot read (not even Edward), becomes the ability to create a mental shield for herself and the people she loves.

Renée Dwyer (previously Swan)

Renée doesn't feature often, but when she does, it's always at key points in the story. She's Isabella Swan's mother and she moved with Bella first to California and then to Phoenix, where, in the September before the *Twilight* saga begins, she married the baseball player Phil Dwyer.

Renée loves classical music and likes playing piano. She looks like her daughter – 'but prettier', Bella thinks.

Bella thinks of her mother as 'loving, unpredictable and crazy' and feels like she has to be responsible for her. Renée is extrovert, daring, eccentric – and an unpredictable cook. At the same time Bella also describes her mother as her best friend.

Edward thinks Renée's thoughts are interesting and insightful, but also childlike.

Renée, for her part, likes to call her daughter her 'open book', because Bella's so easy to read, but only by her mother.

CHARLIE SWAN

Bella's father, Charlie, also called Chief Swan, is a policeman in Forks, drives a patrol car and carries a gun, although he's never actually had to use it.

Charlie is an eccentric small-town cop, who spends his free time fishing or watching TV (mainly baseball games). Bella senses that he never got over Renée leaving him.

Cooking is most definitely not a hobby: although he's lived alone for nearly seventeen years since Renée left him, he still doesn't know how the microwave oven works and he puts a closed jar of spaghetti in it.

Charlie's very patient and understanding, but he can also take on a tone of command and get really angry. Then he calls Bella 'young lady', at which Bella's teenage instincts kick in automatically and they usually argue.

PHIL DWYER

Renée's second husband is a not particularly successful baseball professional, who travels a lot with the minor league. When he gets a contract as a trainer in Jacksonville, Florida, he and Renée move out there. Bella and Edward go there together to visit her mother, but she can't imagine ever living there – if only because of the climate.

Phil is interested in current music and gives Bella a CD, which impresses her. In additional information, Stephenie has said that she had Linkin Park in mind when she thought of that CD.

MR MASON

The bald English teacher.

ERIC YORKIE

One of Bella's classmates. He's a gawky boy with greasy hair and spots. He's over-helpful. Bella secretly calls him 'chess-club Eric'. Since he hasn't got a chance with Bella, he flirts with Jessica and Katie.

MR VARNER

Maths teacher.

EDWARD CULLEN

He was born Edward Masen in Chicago in 1901. Like Bella, Edward was an only child. (Interestingly, Stephenie has created her main characters without siblings, although she herself loves big families, is the child of a big family and has three sons of her own. In her writing, the Cullen family at least embodies this preference.)

Carlisle Cullen found Edward in a hospital in Chicago in the summer of 1918. Edward was seventeen, had Spanish flu and was dying. His parents had already succumbed to the pandemic, so Edward was alone and Carlisle decided to change him. Before he was changed, Edward's eyes were green. Perhaps that's why his vampire eyes look more intense and are more changeable than those of his fellow vampires. When he looks at Bella he has to look down, as the height difference between them is precisely twenty-three centimetres.

Edward was the first person to be changed by Carlisle, founder of the Cullen family, and is very aware of his own lack of self-control. It's only with immense effort, for example, that he manages to leave Bella's four attackers alone and alive. He also knows that his very existence puts Bella in danger. Although Edward seems completely perfect, like being the fastest at the Cullens' baseball game, it's rarely noticed how despairing he is inside. His supernatural powers are external, inside he's all too human. He is torn, pulled this way and that, full of doubts, indecisive and flawed, so really anything but perfect. No wonder Bella describes him as a man she'll never get used to.

EMMETT CULLEN

Born in 1915 in Tennessee, Emmett is the muscleman and, at

six foot five, the tallest member of the family. When the Cullens play baseball, he's the one with the most powerful swing. In 1935 he was fatally wounded while on a bear hunt in the Appalachian Mountains. Rosalie found him and brought him to Carlisle, who changed him, making him the fourth member of the family. Rosalie and Emmett sometimes live separately from the family as a married couple. Edward suspects that in a few years Emmett and Rosalie will get married again. Emmett is fond of Bella and is like an older brother for her.

ROSALIE HALE

Eighteen forever, blonde and breathtakingly beautiful, Rosalie was born in 1915 in Rochester, New York. Her special ability is endurance, which can become stubbornness. Rosalie thinks Edward made a huge mistake in revealing himself to Bella. She thinks that Edward has put all the Cullens in danger and is proved right, since the attack by the newborns from Seattle could have been fatal to them all.

Rosalie, of all the Cullen family, has the most reservations about Bella, but when Bella is pregnant, it's Rosalie who stands up for her against Edward and others who want her to have an abortion. Rosalie finds it hardest to accept that they're all vampires and therefore immortal. She doesn't like it when an outsider, like Bella, knows about her and her life. Rosalie is also jealous of Bella; partly because Edward was never interested in her but fell in love with Bella instantly. Bella is human – and that's what Rosalie would still like to be.

Rosalie was the third to join the Cullen family when Carlisle found her dying on a street in Rochester. Carlisle had hoped she would become for Edward what Esme is for him. Edward, however, only ever saw her as a sister.

In 1933 Rosalie was a young lady of eighteen, who was about to be married. But she was raped repeatedly by her drunken fiancé and three of his friends, who then left her fatally injured.

Rosalie has never drunk human blood, but she did kill all her attackers. When she killed them she was careful not to spill a drop of blood because she didn't want to be tempted – she didn't want to have their blood in her body. Rosalie is a couple with Emmett, whom she saved from a bear so Carlisle could change him for her.

JASPER HALE

Eighteen forever, tall and blond, Jasper was born in 1843 in Texas. It was only in the 1950s that he, together with Alice, was taken in by the Cullens as the latest member of the family. His special power is being able to sense and control the emotions and moods of the people around him. Because he looks like Rosalie, Carlisle and Esme decided to say he and Rosalie are twins. In actual fact, he was changed many years before Rosalie and not by Carlisle, but by another vampire, Maria, during the American Civil War in 1863. He stayed with her through the wild and brutal vampire wars and since then he has been searching for a fulfilled life as a vampire: his special gift of sensitivity to the way others are feeling meant that killing people became too awful and drove him into a depression.

Jasper and Alice met in a diner in the twentieth century and realised they that they were soulmates. They love each other passionately, but are much more private about it than Rosalie and Emmett.

On Bella's eighteenth birthday Jasper is the first to lose control. He wants to bite Bella after she cuts herself on the wrapping paper.

As Jasper's war experiences have made him an expert on fighting young vampires, he's the one who takes on teaching his fellow combatants before the battle against Victoria's creations.

ALICE CULLEN

Alice is a key figure in the *Twilight* saga. This is due to her ability to see into the future, though the visions Alice sees of the future are not always clear.

Alice has short, black hair, an elfin face, is delicately built and slim. Bella finds her high soprano voice almost as attractive as Edward's. Bella describes Alice's eyes (as she does those of the other Cullens) in terms of stones. Alice's are obsidian, a volcanic glass rock.

Alice's ability to see things in the future is subjective. She can't see sudden changes of mind. She can't see what werewolves are going to do either. Alice's gift doesn't work for anyone even near werewolves, so that when Bella secretly visits Jacob at La Push against Edward's will, she gets a kind of radio silence, which is mostly a positive thing for Bella and Jacob, but can also be dangerous.

When Alice saw Jasper for the first time, she knew he was looking for her, before he knew it himself.

Alice is very sensitive to non-human creatures. She always knows when there's a vampire near and whether or not they pose a threat.

Alice doesn't remember her human life and doesn't know who her parents were. When she woke up a vampire, she was alone. If she hadn't found Carlisle, she would probably have become a wild creature.

Bella learns from the evil tracker, James, that as a child Alice had had visions and, as a result, had been put in an asylum in Mississippi sometime after 1910. Once there, she was kept in a dark cell for many years. James wanted to kill her then, but a vampire carer changed her to save her from James.

DR CARLISLE CULLEN

Carlisle is the oldest of the Cullens. As founder of the family, he's the highest authority in times of difficulty. He's the adoptive father of Edward, Emmett, Rosalie, Jasper and Alice and husband of Esme Cullen, whom he changed himself.

Carlisle, only son of an Anglican pastor, was born in mid-seventeenth century London, shortly before Cromwell came to power. His father was extremely intolerant and, as a Protestant, persecuted fanatic Catholics and believers of other faiths. He believed in evil personified and led witch-hunts against werewolves and vampires. Many innocent people were killed and burned.

The history of Carlisle's change is a key element of the *Twilight* saga, for it was he who found the will to feed only on animals and never again on humans. His special ability is to feel compassion, which has led to his changing numerous humans, who, he felt, didn't deserve the death that was coming to them. Bella describes him as having the most humanity and the biggest heart of all the Cullens. To her he seems more handsome than a movie star. She is overwhelmed by the 'amazing perfection of his appearance'. Carlisle is also a brilliant surgeon at the local Forks hospital. His physical age is not given precisely, but he's generally considered to be in his twenties.

ESME CULLEN

Carlisle's wife Esme became the second member of the family after Edward. She lost a baby, her first and only child. Her heart was broken and she wanted to die. Esme threw herself off a cliff and was brought to the morgue, although her heart was actually still beating. Carlisle recognised Esme from a previous meeting and couldn't bear to see her die. She had been born in Ohio in 1895 and was changed by Carlisle at twenty-six years of age. They have been a couple ever since and, just as Carlisle took on the role of father, so Esme became the mother in the Cullen clan.

Esme is small and slim, with rounder features than those of the other Cullens. She has caramel-coloured hair and reminds Bella of the ingénue film-stars from silent movies. Esme's special gift is to love passionately. That's why she's so happy that Edward, single until now, has finally found someone to love, even if she's not quite, as Bella puts it, 'the right one' for him. But Esme knows that Bella's the one he wants, so everything else will somehow work out.

Jessica Stanley

Bella's classmate. Jessica fancies Edward, but has to make do with Mike Newton. They soon stop going out, however, which is when Eric Yorkie comes on the scene.

Jessica has black, curly hair, is extremely nosey and a bit of a gossip. In *Eclipse* she's part of the anti-Bella faction at school led by Lauren Mallory.

Angela Weber

One of Bella's classmates – the friendliest and most honest of the high school clique. She has the most understanding for Bella's peculiar behaviour, standing by her during hard times. Angela has soft brown eyes, straight light-brown hair and goes out with Ben Cheney.

Mr Banner

Biology teacher.

MIKE NEWTON

A classmate of Bella's, he gels his blond hair into careful spikes, is good-looking and has a baby-face. Mike adores Bella and behaves 'like a golden retriever' towards her. When Bella keeps turning him down, he goes out with Jessica, but it they soon call it off.

Mike's father owns the sports shop a little outside town, Olympic Outfitters, whose main customers are backpackers and where Bella works part-time.

COACH CLAPP

P.E. teacher.

TYLER CROWLEY

He appears as Bella's particularly unhappy third high school admirer after he lost control of his van in the car park, nearly crushing her to death. From that point on he is plagued by feelings of guilt, wishes he could turn back the clock and falls in love with her in the process. She sometimes wonders, jokingly and sarcastically, whether she should run him over, so that he would leave her alone and stop feeling guilty.

MS COPE

She's the secretary on the reception desk at Forks High School. She's a large lady with red hair and glasses.

LEE STEVENS

One of Bella's classmates, he can't stand the sight of blood either and later goes out with Samantha Wells.

LAUREN MALLORY

One of Bella's classmates, she has shiny corn-silk blond hair and an unpleasant nasal voice. She is jealous of Bella, because of her relationship with Edward, so she becomes the spokesperson for the anti-Bella faction.

BEN CHANEY

A classmate of Bella's who goes out with Angela Weber.

CONNOR

Another classmate of Bella's, who goes out first with Jessica and later with Lauren.

JACOB BLACK

Bella's childhood friend, known as Jake, he's an American Indian of the Quileute tribe. At the beginning of the *Twilight* saga, he looks fifteen. He wears his hair long, often in a ponytail, tied with an elastic band at the nape of his neck. He has beautiful, smooth, russet-brown skin, dark eyes and a pleasantly rough voice.

Jacob has two older sisters, eighteen year-old twins, Rachel and Rebecca. As children, Bella and the three Black siblings were often together during her holidays in Forks. Rachel is at

Washington State University. Rebecca married a Samoan surfer and lives in Hawaii.

Jacob likes making things and builds cars out of spare parts. He's funny and his cheerfulness is infectious.

In *Twilight* Jacob thinks his dad is a superstitious old man, because he doesn't like the Cullens and believes all the old stories. In *New Moon* he finds out that he himself is actually a werewolf. He quickly grows to six-foot-seven and his muscles are far more developed than other sixteen-year-olds. When people see him, they think he must be dangerous, but Bella never does. She loves Jacob as a friend and in *Eclipse* also as a man. Bella, Edward and Jacob form a love-triangle characterised by jealousy and enmity. Bella tries to reconcile her two admirers, which doesn't happen until *Breaking Dawn*, after her daughter is born.

Incidentally, Bella doesn't only think that Edward smells good, but finds Jacob's smell nice too: woody and musky, appropriate for the forest.

SAM ULEY

Sam, at nineteen, is the oldest in the group of American Indian boys in La Push. Sam is particularly hostile towards the Cullens. At the beginning of *Breaking Dawn* he's the leader of the Quileute werewolf pack. He has imprinted, something that can only happen to werewolves. Until he became a werewolf he was in love with Leah Clearwater, but then he found he had imprinted on Emily Young and had to leave Leah.

If the Cullens hadn't moved to Forks, he wouldn't have become a wolf, wouldn't have imprinted and wouldn't have had to leave Leah. So he hates them and hates himself, but he's still forced into a number of compromises, from protecting Bella, the friend of vampires, all the way to fighting side by side with the Cullens against Victoria and her young vampires.

BILLY BLACK

Before arriving in Forks, Bella hadn't seen Jacob's father Billy for five years, but still she recognises him immediately. Billy is Charlie's best friend. His face is covered in wrinkles, 'like an old leather jacket' and, as a result of an illness, he's now in a wheelchair. Billy himself is not a werewolf, but knows all the old stories and warns Bella repeatedly against allying herself with the Cullens. Bella does have some understanding for his viewpoint, because she sees that it stems from a genuine concern for her welfare. His warnings do cause her some worry, but in comparison to her love for Edward, it's negligible.

DR SNOW

Snow is a doctor and works with Carlisle in the Forks Hospital. He treats Bella after her motorbike accident.

LAURENT

Laurent, a Frenchman, Victoria and James form an unholy vampire triumvirate, which causes the Cullens and Bella enormous distress.

Laurent has an olive skin tone, despite the usual vampire pallor. He's the most beautiful of the three, Bella thinks: gleaming black hair, muscled, gleaming white teeth, and eyes neither golden nor black but of a deep red colour. Laurent is envious of the Cullens' money and lifestyle. He allows himself to be used by Victoria in her quest for revenge and ends up being killed by the werewolves.

JAMES

James is tall and dark-haired and an expert tracker. He loves a challenge and, from his point of view, Bella makes the perfect prey being protected by the Cullens. The Cullens realise he won't rest until he's achieved his goal, and that it will end bloodily. Edward also knows from the outset that he will have no choice but to kill James.

VICTORIA

Victoria's trademark feature is her flaming red, sometimes orange, hair. She is James's mate and, when he's killed, she swears revenge.

Bella calls Victoria a sadistic vampire woman. She won't give up until Edward has lost the love of his life, just as she did.

VOLTURI

In contrast to her description of the settings within the USA, Stephenie allowed her imagination a freer reign when describing Italy. So in the story, Volterra is named after the

Volturi. In actual fact, the name Volterra comes from the Etruscans, who named the town Velathri in the seventh century. The imaginary Volturi – living in a fictional Volterra in a number of details – are a vampire clan founded by Aro, Caius and Marcus, amongst others, about 1,000 B.C. Some of the guardians of the Volturi are Alec, Demetri, Felix, Heidi and Jane, who all possess disturbing special powers.

Denali

In Athapascan, the name means 'big' or 'high', which is why Mount McKinley in Alaska is also called Denali. The Denali clan of vampires, who live near the Denali National Park, called themselves after this mountain. Members of this clan include Tanya, Katrina and Irina, its founders. Eleazer and Carmen joined them later. The clan also takes in nomads like James, but try to remain 'vegetarian' like the Cullens. At the end of *Breaking Dawn* there is a comprehensive index listing all of the vampires and vampire clans across the world.

Emily Young

Emily is engaged to Sam Uley, although her face was mauled by him as a werewolf. Three dark scars run from her right eye down to her mouth. Her once beautiful face is now permanently disfigured, but she acts like a mother to the pack. Emily is Leah Clearwater's second cousin.

Ephraim Black
Jacob's great-grandfather and Quileute Elder who made the original treaty with the Cullens.

Mike
Charlie's colleague, assistant Sheriff.

Quil Ateara
A werewolf in Sam's pack, and one of Jacob's best friends. He likes being a werewolf and has chocolate-coloured fur. He has imprinted on Emily's two-year-old niece, Claire.

Embry Call
Also a werewolf in Sam's pack who has grey fur with dark spots on his back. He is also a good friend of Jacob.

Jared
Jared is one of the werewolves in the original Quileute pack. He imprints on Kim, a girl in his class at school.

Paul
The most hot-tempered werewolf in the Quileute pack.

Mr Greene
Headmaster of Forks High School.

MR BERTY

A teacher, he recites the Robert Frost poem.

KAREN NEWTON

Co-owner of the sports shop where Bella works, she is Mike's mother.

KATIE MARSHALL

Starts working at the same sports shop.

LEAH CLEARWATER

Harry and Sue's daughter, she was at school with Sam Uley and dated him for a number of years before he imprinted on her cousin Emily, leaving Leah heartbroken. She is the only known female werewolf in the Quileute tribe and big sister to Seth Clearwater. She joins Jacob's pack when he breaks away.

SETH CLEARWATER

Harry and Sue's son, Leah's little brother. He is one of the first werewolves to trust the Cullens and becomes good friends with Edward. He also joins Jacob's pack.

HARRY CLEARWATER

An old friend of Charlie's, who dies of a heart-attack.

TANYA
She's a vampire with strawberry-blond hair from the Denali clan in Alaska. She was, or maybe still is, in love with Edward. Even at her wedding, Bella's still jealous of Tanya.

IRINA
She is a vampire from the Denali clan and wants to wipe out the werewolf pack, because they killed Laurent, whom she loved.

SUE CLEARWATER
The widow of Charlie's friend, Harry Clearwater.

✦

LOCATIONS

As a result of Stephenie's disclosure that most of the locations in the *Twilight* series are true to life (all the ones listed here exist in real life), many of the places have become tourist attractions for *Twilight* fans.

FORKS

Stephenie chose Forks, a small town in North-West Washington State on the Olympic Peninsula as the main setting for her *Twilight* series because it has the highest rainfall in the USA – perfect for her vampires. Stephenie herself only visited Forks after *Twilight* had been published. She was surprised by how similar it was to her imagined Forks. It was like walking into her own book and she kept expecting Edward and Bella to appear at any moment.

Every September 13th, Bella's birthday, Forks celebrates Stephenie Meyer Day. Fans dress up as characters from the books, bands play the songs which are linked to Stephenie and her books and, if Stephenie's there in person, huge queues form to get her signature.

LA PUSH

La Push is a real community in Clallam County, Washington State. The name comes from the French *la bouche*, meaning 'the mouth' and refers to the mouth of the Quileute River around which La Push is built. It is a small Indian reservation on the coast, where Billy Black, his son Jacob and other characters live. It lies about fifteen miles from Forks. The road runs through dense forest, partly following the Quileute River. The long crescent of First Beach is its landmark feature. At the southern end of the bay there are some craggy cliffs, which rise up out of the ocean like a finger.

PORT ANGELES

This is where, following her timely rescue from four dangerous thugs, Edward and Bella have their first meal together in 'La Bella Italia'. Port Angeles is smarter and more picturesque than Forks and attracts many tourists. It has a pretty boardwalk along the beach and a department store. Port Angeles is also where people from Forks go to the cinema.

PHOENIX

Bella loves the city she grew up in. Stephenie's own passion for Phoenix is clear in Bella's memories and descriptions. She describes Phoenix, 'Valley of the Sun', the biggest city in Arizona and the fifth biggest in the USA as a desert metropolis with more than three hundred days of sun annually, as being busy, 'endlessly spreading' and about five times bigger than Seattle.

SEATTLE

Like Phoenix, Seattle represents the big city in the series, with all the advantages and disadvantages that brings. Victoria's army of young vampires commit so many murders that Seattle is catapulted into first place in the national murder statistics.

TACOMA

The concert Bella wanted to take Edward to, took place in this town on Mount Rainier approximately fifty kilometres south of Seattle, but Victoria's attack put paid to any concert visits.

GOAT ROCKS WILDERNESS

An area south of Mount Rainier where the Cullens like to hunt.

Charlie doesn't think it's a good place for camping (the Cullens' cover story), because there are too many bears, and that most people would only go there during the hunting season.

SOL DUC RIVER

The Sol Duc River winds its way through unspoilt forest, down from the Olympic Mountains, and flows right past the Cullens' house, which lies North of Forks.

PORTLAND

The alternative to Seattle if you want a day out shopping.

CARS

The theme of cars first appears on the second page of the first chapter of the first book, when Bella mentions that her mother often forgets to fill her car up. Petrol is mentioned regularly: when Edward doesn't want Bella to travel alone to Seattle, he talks about her old Chevy truck's high fuel consumption, saying that the wasting of finite resources is a topic everybody should be concerned with.

Bella's – or rather Stephenie Meyer's – interest in cars is apparent in a number of scenes which don't actually have anything directly to do with cars. When the tracker James speaks to her on the phone, she finds his voice friendly at first, somehow anonymously familiar, like the voice 'from an advert for luxury limousines'. Or just before the battle with Victoria and her newborn vampires, when Jacob gets the chance of a really passionate kiss, her heart lurches straight 'into fourth gear'.

Stephenie's fondness for speed is shown in the featured driving styles. Edward hates driving slowly. At first, Bella's afraid when Edward is driving, but he has good reason to be fearless and is used to driving fast – one hundred miles an hour and faster when the situation calls for it. Apart from that, his

Volvo moves so smoothly and evenly that the speed is barely noticeable. Edward has an in-built radar-detector with his mind-reading to warn him of any police cars.

It's remarkable how many different models of car are mentioned, but it's not about product placement, more that Stephenie wants to specific because cars are important to her. Makes of car are frequently named, but other types of brand name are scarce. There would be plenty of opportunities, for example, fashion brands could have been mentioned when Bella and her friends go shopping in Port Angeles. Or in later descriptions of Edward's wardrobe and friends' clothes. Bella only once mentions her pyjamas from Victoria's Secret, a birthday present from her mother, which she stupidly left in Phoenix. She's never worn them, but would have liked to be able to wear them when Edward stayed in her bedroom with her for the first time. The wedding dress Alice organises for Bella is by Perrine Bruyère.

Cars also influence the mood of the characters, even the generally poised Edward. When Rosalie's red cabriolet is in the school car park, surrounded by a ring of curious boys, he says the BMW is ostentatious, but his envy is clear.

Drunk driving also has its place in the story. Not that either Edward or Bella drink, but they're high – high on each other, on their love for each other – high enough that Edward doesn't let Bella drive, and points out that 'friends don't let friends drive drunk'. After all, she's high on his very presence.

One of the reasons cars are of such importance in the

Twilight series, explains Stephenie, is that two of her brothers, Jacob and Paul are crazy about cars.

Here are the most significant cars from the series, in the order in which they appear:

CHEVROLET

Bella's car that her father gives her when she first arrives in Forks is an old Chevy Transporter, built 1953, which used to belong to Billy Black. It's painted red, has rounded fenders, a bulbous cab and a very loud engine (even when idling). Her pick-up truck drives slowly (much to Edward's distress), but provides excellent protection for the accident-prone Bella.

MERCEDES AND PORSCHE

Mercedes and Porsches fresh from the factory were quite normal at Bella's high school in Paradise Valley. In Forks, the car park is filled with older and cheaper models, with the obvious exception of the Cullens' cars.

VOLVO

The Volvo is the most attractive car in the car park at Forks High School. It's metallic silver-grey, brand new and belongs to Edward Cullen. The Volvo S60R is the least conspicuous of the Cullens' cars, which is why, at the beginning of the story, it's the car the four of them always come to school in.

TOYOTA COROLLA

At the beginning of the story, there's a half-rusted Toyota parked behind Bella's Chevy on the school parking lot. Bella had already noted that her robust Chevy was the type of car 'that never gets damaged' and that it would easily survive an accident without damage, while any foreign car would be all over the road in pieces. Bella imagines that the Toyota is the kind of car her Chevy 'would make scrap metal of'.

TYLER CROWLEY'S TRUCK

In the dramatic scene when Edward saves Bella's life for the first time, it skids on the ice and crashes into her Chevy which remains unscathed. Tyler's truck, on the other hand (the make isn't mentioned), ends up being sold for spare parts.

CHEVROLET SUBURBAN

Mike Newton's car.

NISSAN SENTRA

A used car, bought to replace Tyler's van.

MERCURY

Jessica drives an old white model.

BMW M3 CABRIOLET

Rosalie drives this bright red cabriolet – of course, in Forks she generally has to keep the roof closed. Even Edward thinks it's a little pretentious, and admits it's a self-indulgence. All the Cullens like to drive fast and love the kinds of cars they can do that in.

FORD
Billy and Jacob Black drive an ageing black model.

JEEP
Emmett's car is a massive Jeep Wrangler. The headlamps are protected by metal grilles. There are four additional floodlights fixed to the bumper. The bright red car is fitted with six-point seat belts for off-road driving. When Bella first sees it, she calls it a 'real monster'. The wheels stand higher than Bella's hips.

MERCEDES
Carlisle's Mercedes S55 AMG is a black, state-of-the-art vehicle whose windows are 'darker than a film-star's car'. Even at high speeds the engine makes almost no sound.

PORSCHE
Edward gives Alice a canary-yellow Porsche 911, which she's wanted desperately, since she first saw, stole and tested one in Italy when they needed an escape car.

ASTON MARTIN
For special occasions, Edward also has a black Aston Martin V12 Vanquish. He drives Bella to the Spring Ball in this car and it's so low she feels like she's sitting on the ground.

VOLKSWAGEN

Although Jacob is mad about cars, he can only afford to drive a simple VW Golf.

THE BEFORE CAR

Bella's security car for before she's changed into a vampire gets a lot of people staring, and not only in Forks. According to Stephenie, it's a fictitious car, but it is very similar to the bullet and explosion proof Mercedes S600 Guard.

THE AFTER CAR

Bella's car for after she's changed doesn't have to be such a safe car, but should be fast and beautiful, so Edward gets her a Ferrari F430.

THE MOTORBIKES

Jacob rides a Harley Sprint, Bella a light Honda and Edward has a heavy Ducati.

DEDICATIONS

Stephenie dedicated *Twilight* to her big sister, Emily, without whose enthusiasm not even the first part would have been finished, as Stephenie herself says.

New Moon is dedicated to Stephenie's father, Stephen Morgan. No one ever received more loving or unconditional support than Stephenie received from Stephen.

In terms of dedication, *Eclipse* is an exception as it is divided into two sections. In the first sentence, Stephenie dedicates the book to her husband, Pancho, for, amongst other reasons, his willingness to eat out, from which we can assume that during intensive writing phases the author cooked even less for her husband than Bella did for Charlie. Stephenie thanks him in turn for his patience and love, his friendship and his humour. It is conspicuous that 'patience and love' are linked, as though neither characteristic could exist without the other.

In the second sentence, however, she dedicates the book to her three sons Gabe, Seth and Eli, with the comment that through them she has experienced the kind of love a person would die for. It's interesting that Stephenie Meyer mentions this highest order of love, love a person would die for, in relation to her children rather than her husband, whereas Bella and Edward experience it in their passion for one another, for Bella and Edward are prepared to give their lives for their love at any moment.

Stephenie dedicates *Breaking Dawn* to her agent and her favourite band, Muse.

When reading all four dedications together, it's noticeable that Stephenie Meyer mentions her sister, her husband, her children and her father, even her agent and her favourite band, but not with one word does she mention her mother.

FILM

In November 2008, the film *Twilight* was released first in the USA, then worldwide; it enjoyed tremendous success, and the other three books are also going to be made into films.

Kristen Stewart, the female lead, was one of the first to be chosen. In an interview, the young actress said she had been allowed to give her opinion in the choice of male lead. Allegedly there were more than five thousand actors on the list of possible male leads. In the end, it was Kristen Stewart who spotted Robert Pattinson and she quickly carried her point. She explained her choice by saying that Edward wasn't perfect. She herself thought that in the book Edward was anything but the perfect man, and emphasised his weaknesses, his uncertainties, his doubts, his unhappiness. 'The main thing about the character of Edward is that he's so small on the inside. All his strength is on the surface. Robert came into the casting studio and clearly felt uncomfortable, as if he was in the wrong place. And I thought: that's the one, that's him!'

Both the lead actors read the books first, with Kristen describing the books as hardcore and Robert saying they were very personal.

Stephenie thinks the best casting was Ashley Greene as

Alice. 'Oh my God, they've found Alice,' she said when she saw the first pictures.

Many websites have already begun to concentrate more strongly on the films than on the books, but without Stephenie's books, the whole cinema hype would be impossible. The fascination of the books coupled with the films have caused hysteria for the stars, which the US media have compared to Beatlemania in the 1960s.

Music

'I can't work without music,' says Stephenie. Her favourite musical muse is the band Muse. Stephenie jokes she's probably the only mother with a Muse bumper sticker on a family-sized estate car. Other favourites include Linkin Park, My Chemical Romance, Coldplay, The All American Rejects, Travis, The Strokes, Brand New, U2, Kasabian, Jimmy Eat World and Weezer. While she's writing, she explained in 2008 to *Rolling Stone* magazine, she listens to bands and songs which suit the characters she's writing about. Detailed playlists with audio extracts for all four books are widely available online. It's interesting that Stephenie has a preference for a quite hard rock sound. She thinks that may be due to her parents' conservative approach to music – they were very careful in their choice of pop music appropriate for the family to listen to. It was only when she was at college that she finally had the freedom to develop her own musical tastes and they turned out to be a far cry from sounds suitable for a practising Mormon. Stephenie found her first experience of Muse electrifying. The song 'Hate Me', by Blue October, had a similar effect on her. The first time she heard it, she says, she thought it was Edward's voice coming from the car radio. 'Romantically dark,' is how lead singer Justin Furstenfeld describes Blue October's songs, just like Stephenie's *Twilight* saga. The soundtrack to the *Twilight* film reached the top of the international music charts before the film was even released.

Before the release of *Breaking Dawn*, the US publishers organised a series of concerts in different cities at each of which Stephenie was to be present. She was most excited about the live performance by Justin Furstenfeld of Blue October, because their songs were some of the most important to her while she was writing. The events, which were a mixture of public readings by the author, open discussion and rock concert, were received enthusiastically by fans.

Stephenie's passion for rock music has led to further projects. For example, she was involved in developing the music video for 'The Resolution' by Jack's Mannequin in which the singer and pianist are pursued by the breaking surf.

Music plays an important role within the *Twilight* books themselves as well. Edward loves 'Clair de Lune' by Debussy, which is also one of Bella's favourite pieces of music. The whole spectrum is covered, from Chopin's 'Nocturnes' to pop classics. In the car, Edward tunes the radio to an Oldies station and sings along with a song – sadly we're not told which – that Bella's never heard before, but Edward's word perfect and sings the praises of Fifties music.

The Cullens' have a grand piano in their house and Edward is a talented pianist and composer. Bella herself inspired him to compose a lullaby.

One whole wall in Edward's bedroom is covered in CD shelves. The CDs are ordered according to the year of release and, within the year, according to preference. Obviously Edward owns state-of-the-art hi-fi equipment, and when Bella visits his house for the first time, he puts on some light jazz.

Alice is also very musical. Effortlessly she adds a complex harmony to a particular song, an octave above the original melody. It's also worth noting that Bella, trying to hum the wedding march, concludes it sounds more like a funeral march.

Afterword

Nothing conveys the appeal of Stephenie Meyer's *Twilight* saga so clearly as her fans themselves. The enthusiasm this literary phenomenon is stirring up will continue to grow. There may be criticism here and there. Analyses of links between Mormonism and the *Twilight* saga will appear. Essays for journals and newspapers, dissertations for university courses will be written about Stephenie Meyer's novels. The marketing aspect will be analysed carefully. Has the last word been spoken about that fateful day of June 2nd 2003, about Stephenie Meyer's dream? Hardly.

Stephenie Meyer's popularity is often compared with JK Rowling, but many find Stephenie's novels even better – Meyer's writing is prettier and less action-driven. Meyer's worlds and their populations are not divided so obviously into good and bad. Meyer writes about confused feelings, endless discussions and gnawing doubt and many teenage and adult readers take pleasure in questioning life in the company of Meyer's characters.

One thing's for sure: these won't be the last words to be written about Stephenie Meyer's books. I have the feeling that her writing career has only just begun. Expectation is riding high that Stephenie Meyer's pen will be providing further adventures – with or without Bella!

In the meantime, readers of all ages, and from all over the world, will continue to become enchanted and remain captivated by the many different facets of the *Twilight* saga.

Acknowledgements

Thanks to Isabella (Türkhan Agvaz) and Angela (Verena Schulz), co-founders of the website www.team-edward.net.

Thanks to Dr Jazz, who called me at night, putting things into perspective. His musical tastes aren't quite Stephenie's, but www.drjazz.ch is well worth a visit.

Thanks to my agent Dr Eckhart Prahl (the best!).

Thanks to Heyne Verlag who have already published such a lovely edition of *Schlemm*.

Thank you Vera, for perhaps forgiving my having lingered such a long time with the undead.

Thanks in advance for any improvements or supplementary information (send to bardola@t-online.de).

TEAM JACOB?

DISCOVER WHAT TAYLOR LAUTNER IS REALLY LIKE

Find out everything about the man behind the wolf!
Discover what made Taylor Lautner become an actor,
how he landed the role of Jacob Black and how he
buffed up for *New Moon*! And get closer to the real
Taylor with the lowdown on his loves, his hopes,
how he deals with fame, and what's next for the
hottest new star of Hollywood.

Taylor Lautner –
Inside Out

The unauthorised biography

TEAM EDWARD?

GET CLOSER TO
ROBERT PATTINSON

Find out everything about the man behind the world's
sexiest vampire – from Robert's bad boy school days
to the audition that changed his life and his overnight
success as Edward Cullen in *Twilight*. Discover his
musical talents and how he's dealing with instant fame,
and get closer to the real Robert with the essential
facts on what makes him tick, what turns him on,
and what's next for the hottest guy in Hollywood.

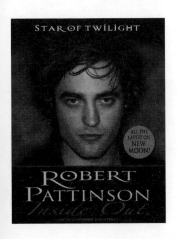

Robert Pattinson –
Inside Out
The unauthorised biography

☆

www.piccadillypress.co.uk

☆ The latest news on forthcoming books

☆ Chapter previews

☆ Author biographies

☆ Fun quizzes

☆ Reader reviews

☆ Competitions and fab prizes

☆ Book features and cool downloads

☆ And much, much more . . .

Log on and check it out!

Piccadilly Press

☆